# AQA GCSE (9-1) Maths

**Foundation**

**Suitable for Grades 1–5**

# Revision Workbook

**Authors: Jemma Sherwood and Paul Hunt**
**Series Editor: Naomi Bartholomew-Millar**

## The Oxford Revise GCSE Maths Series: Our approach

Our no-fuss approach lets you dive straight into the practice you need for the exam. GCSE Grades help you monitor your own progress on every page, and 'Guided answers' at the back help you mark your own solutions. The practice exam papers come with guidance too: for every question we let you know which page to turn to for extra practice. And you'll find perfectly matched support on the exact same page in the revision guide.

**OXFORD**
UNIVERSITY PRESS

# Contents

---

**Guided practice papers**

For every question in the Practice exam papers, we've provided a note of what page to turn to for more practice on that topic.

Further practice & support: Q1 p.60; Q2 p.17

You'll also find 'Guided answers' at the back of the book, so you can mark your own solutions.

---

**Use of calculators**

This book provides support with both how and when to use your calculator. Look for these symbols against questions:

Make sure to use your calculator – it's good practice for the exam.

Make sure not to use your calculator – this question would only appear in the non-calculator paper.

If there's no symbol, then the question could appear on either the calculator or the non-calculator paper.

# Place value

**Grade 1**

**1.** Write the number ninety thousand, one hundred and twenty-four using digits.

92,124 ............................ [I got _1_ / 1 mark]

**Grade 2**

**2.** Write down the value represented by the digit 2 in each of these numbers.

a) 4269

............... ~~60~~ 200 ............... [_1_ / 1 mark]

b) 723 000

............... 23,000 ............... [_1_ / 1 mark]

c) 5.201

............... 0·201 ............... [_1_ / 1 mark]

**Grade 2**

**3.** Put one of the symbols <, > or = in each box to make a correct statement.

a) 0.36 $\boxed{>}$ 0.306 [_1_ / 1 mark]

b) 0.450 $\boxed{=}$ 0.45 [_1_ / 1 mark]

c) 1.9003 $\boxed{<}$ 1.903 [_1_ / 1 mark]

**Grade 2**

**4.** Put these numbers in order of size, starting with the smallest.

④ 7.504   ② 7.450   ③ 7.405   ① 7.054

.................................................................................................... [_2_ / 2 marks]

**Grade 2**

**5.** Work out

**Hint**
Think about how many places the
digits move and in what direction.

a) 67.9 × 1000   67,900

.................................................................... [_1_ / 1 mark]

b) 0.9 ÷ 100   0.009

.................................................................... [_1_ / 1 mark]

**Grade 2**

**6.** 10 packets of sweets cost £8.50. How much does one packet cost? Circle your answer.

9p   (85p)   8.5p   £85   [_1_ / 1 mark]

**Grade 3**

**7.** Given that 4.5 × 192 = 864, work out the answer to each of these calculations.

a) 4.5 × 19.2

............... 86.4 ............... [_1_ / 1 mark]

b) 450 × 0.0192

............... 8.64 ............... [_1_ / 1 mark]

c) 8.64 ÷ 0.45

............... 19.2 ............... [_1_ / 1 mark]

$\overline{|\ 8.64}$

**1**

# Order of operations

**1.** Work out

a) $2 + 3 \times 9$    27

............29............ [I got _1_ / 1 mark]

b) $24 \div (6 - 2) \times 5$    6   4 ×5

............30............ [_1_ / 1 mark]

divide

c) $10 - 3^2$    9

............1............ [_1_ / 1 mark]

BODMAS
of ther   Subtract
× 

Grade 2

**2.** Circle the correct calculation.

$(20 - 5) - 2 + 6 = 11$    5   8

$20 - 5 - (2 + 6) = 11$    15   8

$3 + 8 = 11$

$20 - (5 - 2 + 6) = 11$

$20 - (5 - 2) + 6 = 11$    3   9    [_1_ / 1 mark]

Grade 3

**3.** Work out

a) $(12 - 4 \times 2)^3$    8

............ [__ / 1 mark]

b) $\dfrac{4 \times 5^2}{4 \times 5 \div 2}$

............ [__ / 1 mark]

c) $5 \times \sqrt{50 - 1} + 6 \times 3$

............ [__ / 1 mark]

Grade 3

**4.** Use your calculator to work out these expressions.

**Hint**
*If your calculator is 'natural display', make sure the calculation on screen looks just like these.*

a) $\dfrac{2 \times 36 + 18}{20 - 12}$

............ [__ / 1 mark]

b) $\left(\dfrac{3}{5}\right)^3 + 9 \div 3$

............ [__ / 1 mark]

c) $\sqrt{7.29} \times 1000$

............ [__ / 1 mark]

Grade 3

**5.** Bavan says that $2 \times 3^2 = 36$ but Eva says $2 \times 3^2 = 18$

Who is correct? Give your reasoning.

............

............ [__ / 1 mark]

# Rounding and truncating

**Grade 2**

**1.** Round 258.3 to

   **a)** the nearest integer

   ..................................................... **[I got ___ / 1 mark]**

   **b)** the nearest 10

   ..................................................... **[ ___ / 1 mark]**

   **c)** the nearest 100

   ..................................................... **[ ___ / 1 mark]**

**Grade 2**

**2.** Round 19.902 to

   **a)** the nearest integer

   ..................................................... **[ ___ / 1 mark]**

   **b)** 1 decimal place

   ..................................................... **[ ___ / 1 mark]**

   **c)** 2 decimal places.

   ..................................................... **[ ___ / 1 mark]**

**Grade 2**

**3.** Truncate 8.2694 to

   **a)** an integer

> **Hint**
> Remind yourself of the difference between truncation and rounding.

   ..................................................... **[ ___ / 1 mark]**

   **b)** a tenth

   ..................................................... **[ ___ / 1 mark]**

   **c)** a hundredth.

   ..................................................... **[ ___ / 1 mark]**

**Grade 2**

**4.** One bag of grass seed covers an area of 3.66 m². Work out the size of lawn nine bags of seeds will cover. Give your answer to the nearest integer.

   ..................................................... m²   **[ ___ / 2 marks]**

**Grade 2**

**5.** A jug contains 3000 ml of juice. A glass holds 310 ml. How many glasses can be filled from the jug?

   ..................................................... **[ ___ / 2 marks]**

**Grade 3**

**6.** Mark is paid £18.93 an hour and works 7.5 hours a day.
Kwamé is paid £22.17 an hour and works 6.5 hours a day.
Work out the difference between their daily pay.

> **Hint**
> Money is often rounded to 2 dp.

   £ ..................................................... **[ ___ / 3 marks]**

3

# Significant figures

**Grade 3**

**1.** Round 0.050 28 to 2 significant figures. Circle your answer.

0.05          0.051          0.050          0.0503          **[I got __ / 1 mark]**

**Grade 3**

**2.** Round 20 193 to

   **a)** 4 significant figures

   .................................................................... **[ __ / 1 mark]**

   **b)** 3 significant figures

   .................................................................... **[ __ / 1 mark]**

   **c)** 2 significant figures

   .................................................................... **[ __ / 1 mark]**

   **d)** 1 significant figure.

   .................................................................... **[ __ / 1 mark]**

**Grade 3**

**3.** The area of a square is 40 cm². Work out the length of the side of the square. Give your answer to 3 significant figures.

40 cm²

.................................................... cm   **[ __ / 2 marks]**

> **Hint**
> You square the side length to get the area of a square.

**Grade 3**

**4. a)** Work out this expression using your calculator.

$$\frac{4.56 \times 2.89}{12.1 - 0.56}$$

Write your answer as a decimal, giving all the digits on your calculator display.

.................................................................... **[ __ / 1 mark]**

   **b)** Write your answer to part **a** to 2 significant figures.

   .................................................................... **[ __ / 1 mark]**

**Grade 4**

**5.** Shirley rounds 0.065 29 to 2 significant figures and gives the answer 0.07

Give a reason why Shirley is wrong.

> **Hint**
> Think about the difference between significant figures and decimal places.

....................................................................
....................................................................

**[ __ / 1 mark]**

# Estimation

**1.** Estimate the value of 2.84 × 19.3. Circle your answer.

**Hint**
You usually round numbers to 1 sf to estimate.

57          40          60          20

**[I got ___ / 1 mark]**

**2.** Estimate the value of $\frac{317 + 48.6}{9.683}$. Show your working.

**[ ___ / 2 marks]**

**3.** Estimate the value of $\frac{2.67 \times 1.36}{0.11 + 0.42}$. Show your working.

**[ ___ / 2 marks]**

**4.** A biologist visits a lake at the start of January and works out that the number of fish in the lake is approximately 1000. She thinks that the population is growing at a rate of 17 fish per day. Estimate how many fish there will be in the lake five months later.

**[ ___ / 3 marks]**

**5.** In one week, an Italian restaurant sells 96 portions of lasagne. The restaurant sells a portion of lasagne for £8.95 and each portion costs £3.20 to make. Estimate the profit the restaurant makes from lasagne in the week.

£ ........................................................ **[ ___ / 3 marks]**

**6.** James is driving to visit his Gran who lives 405 km away. He leaves at 8.30 am and drives at an average speed of 77 km/h, stopping for a 25-minute lunch break on the way. Estimate the time he arrives at his Gran's.

**[ ___ / 3 marks]**

# Error intervals

**1.** A number is given as 5.3 rounded to 1 decimal place.

Work out the smallest number this could be.

........................................................................ [I got ___ / 1 mark]

**2.** The length, $L$ cm, of a rectangle is 14 cm to the nearest centimetre.

Complete the statement to show the range of possible values of $L$.

................ $\leq L <$ ................ [ ___ / 2 marks]

**3.** The length, $p$ m, of a football pitch is given as 110 m.

Write the error interval for $p$ if this value is rounded to

**a)** the nearest 10 metres

................ $\leq p <$ ................ [ ___ / 2 marks]

**b)** the nearest 5 metres

................ $\leq p <$ ................ [ ___ / 2 marks]

**c)** the nearest metre.

................ $\leq p <$ ................ [ ___ / 2 marks]

**4.** A number, $x$, is given rounded to a particular degree of accuracy.

Write the error interval for $x$ in each case.

**a)** $x = 4.67$ to 2 decimal places

................ $\leq x <$ ................ [ ___ / 2 marks]

**b)** $x = 5000$ to 1 significant figure

................ $\leq x <$ ................ [ ___ / 2 marks]

**5.** The average length, $l$ seconds, of a chart song is 250 seconds to 2 significant figures.

Give the error interval for $l$.

> **Hint**
> Remember to use the correct inequality symbols: minimum $\leq$ x < maximum.

........................................................................ [ ___ / 2 marks]

**6.** Sienna uses her calculator to answer a question. The display breaks and she can only see 1.8 at the start of her answer. Let $x$ be the unknown number on the display. Circle the correct error interval for $x$.

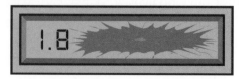

$1.75 \leq x < 1.85$      $1.8 \leq x < 1.9$      $1.7 \leq x < 1.9$      $1.8 \leq x < 1.85$

[ ___ / 1 mark]

# Calculating with negative numbers

**1.** The table shows the minimum temperature (in °C) across five months of the year.

| Month | December | January | February | March | April |
|---|---|---|---|---|---|
| **Minimum temperature (°C)** | −1 | −5 | 0 | 3 | 8 |

   **a)** In which month is the lowest temperature recorded?

   ..................................................... **[I got __ / 1 mark]**

   **b)** Work out the difference in minimum temperature between December and January.

   ..................................................... **[ __ / 1 mark]**

   **c)** Work out the difference in minimum temperature between April and January.

   ..................................................... **[ __ / 1 mark]**

**2.** Work out

   **a)** 2 + (−5)

   ..................................................... **[ __ / 1 mark]**

   **b)** (−48) ÷ (−6)

   ..................................................... **[ __ / 1 mark]**

   **c)** $(-3)^2$

   ..................................................... **[ __ / 1 mark]**

> **Hint**
> Remember the order of operations.

**3.** Work out

   **a)** 5 + (−3) × 4

   ..................................................... **[ __ / 2 marks]**

   **b)** (8 − 10) × 4 − (−10)

   ..................................................... **[ __ / 2 marks]**

**4.** Circle the answer to $\dfrac{-14 + (-10)}{4 - 10}$

   6          −4          1          4          **[ __ / 1 mark]**

**5.** Thomas's bank balance is £241. He goes shopping and uses his bank card to spend £154 in the supermarket, £95 in the computer shop and £8.50 in a café. How much does Thomas need to pay into his bank account to bring the balance up to £100?

   £..................................................... **[ __ / 3 marks]**

# Calculating with decimals

**Grade 2**

**1.** Work out

    **a)**    $2.906 + 8.31$

    .................................................................... **[I got ___ / 2 marks]**

    **b)**    $25.043 - 17.82$

    .................................................................... **[ ___ / 2 marks]**

**Grade 3**

**2.** Work out

    **a)**    $7.4 \times 0.26$

> **Hint**
> For part **b**, it's easier to divide by a whole number.
> How can you change the calculation to do this?

    .................................................................... **[ ___ / 2 marks]**

    **b)**    $17.12 \div 0.8$

    .................................................................... **[ ___ / 2 marks]**

    **c)**    $\dfrac{1.9 + 7.62}{9 - 8.3}$

    .................................................................... **[ ___ / 3 marks]**

**Grade 3**

**3.** Seven identical toys cost a total of £55.65. Work out the cost of one toy.

    £.................................................................... **[ ___ / 2 marks]**

**Grade 3**

**4.** Alex works out the answer to $14.5 \times 2.6$. Alex says the answer is 3.77
    Give a reason why Alex is wrong.

    ....................................................................

    .................................................................... **[ ___ / 1 mark]**

# Introduction to fractions

**1.** Which is the larger fraction, $\frac{1}{5}$ or $\frac{1}{4}$? Give a reason for your answer.

You may use the diagram to help.

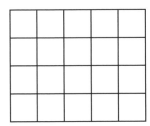

...........................................................................................................  **[I got ___ / 1 mark]**

**2.** Write these fractions in order of size, starting with the smallest.

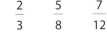

$$\frac{3}{4} \qquad \frac{2}{3} \qquad \frac{5}{8} \qquad \frac{7}{12}$$

> **Hint**
> Find equivalent fractions with a common denominator.

...........................................................................................................  **[ ___ / 2 marks]**

**3. a)** Write each mixed number as an improper fraction, giving your answer in its simplest form.

    **i)** $\quad 1\frac{2}{5}$

...........................................................................................................  **[ ___ / 1 mark]**

    **ii)** $\quad 3\frac{3}{4}$

...........................................................................................................  **[ ___ / 2 marks]**

**b)** Write each improper fraction as a mixed number, giving your answer in its simplest form.

    **i)** $\quad \frac{17}{9}$

...........................................................................................................  **[ ___ / 1 mark]**

    **ii)** $\quad \frac{92}{40}$

...........................................................................................................  **[ ___ / 2 marks]**

**4.** After a party, Dave has $2\frac{1}{3}$ bottles of cola left and Lizzie has $\frac{19}{8}$ bottles left. Who has the most cola? Show your working.

> **Hint**
> Here, you need to compare fractions that are presented differently. Convert both fractions to the same form.

...........................................................................................................  **[ ___ / 3 marks]**

# Proportions of amounts

**1.** Work out

a) $\frac{1}{5}$ of 45

..................................................... **[I got ___ / 2 marks]**

b) 30% of 180

..................................................... **[ ___ / 2 marks]**

c) $\frac{5}{7}$ of 14

..................................................... **[ ___ / 2 marks]**

d) 62% of 50

..................................................... **[ ___ / 2 marks]**

**2.** Every month, Faizal receives a bonus of 15% of his earnings in that month. In April, Faizal earnt £2460. How much was his bonus in April? Circle your answer.

£2091 £369 £2829 £164 **[ ___ / 1 mark]**

**3.** Which is bigger, 110% of 90 or $\frac{8}{7}$ of 84? Show all your working.

> **Hint**
> A diagram such as a bar model can help with these kinds of questions.

 **[ ___ / 3 marks]**

**4.** Every year, a school raises money to donate to charity. One year, it chooses to donate $\frac{3}{8}$ of the money raised to a hospital. If the school raises £7200 that year, how much does it give to the hospital?

£ **[ ___ / 2 marks]**

**5.** 48 children go on an outdoor activities day and must choose a morning activity.

25% of the children choose rock climbing.

$\frac{5}{12}$ of the children choose raft building.

The rest choose kayaking.

Work out how many children choose kayaking.

> **Hint**
> Calculate how many children choose rock climbing and how many choose raft building.

..................................................... **[ ___ / 3 marks]**

# Calculating with fractions 1

**Grade 2**

1. What is the reciprocal of 0.25?

.................................................................. [I got ___ / 1 mark]

**Grade 3**

2. Work out and simplify where possible

 a) $\dfrac{1}{3} \times \dfrac{2}{5}$

................................................................ [ ___ / 1 mark]

 b) $\dfrac{3}{7} \times \dfrac{14}{9}$

................................................................ [ ___ / 2 marks]

**Grade 3**

3. Work out and simplify where possible

 a) $\dfrac{3}{4} \div \dfrac{1}{11}$

................................................................ [ ___ / 2 marks]

 b) $\dfrac{6}{5} \div \dfrac{7}{10}$

................................................................ [ ___ / 2 marks]

**Grade 3**

4. A café uses up $\dfrac{2}{3}$ of a box of coffee beans every day. How many days will it take for the café to use up 16 boxes of coffee beans?

.................................................................. days   [ ___ / 2 marks]

**Grade 3**

5. In a model village, everything is built at a size $\dfrac{1}{9}$ of the original size. If a street is 30 m long in real life, work out how long it is in the model village. Give your answer in its simplest form.

.................................................................. m   [ ___ / 2 marks]

**Grade 4**

6. Rafael reserves $\dfrac{3}{10}$ of his monthly wage to pay his bills. $\dfrac{1}{4}$ of this amount is spent on his electricity bill. What fraction of his monthly wage does Rafael spend on his electricity bill? Circle your answer.

> **Hint**
> What calculation does the word 'of' represent?

$\dfrac{12}{10}$ \qquad $\dfrac{4}{14}$ \qquad $\dfrac{3}{40}$ \qquad $\dfrac{1}{4}$

[ ___ / 1 mark]

**Grade 5**

7. A triangle has base $1\dfrac{1}{5}$ cm and perpendicular height $\dfrac{6}{5}$ cm. A rectangle has the same area as the triangle. If the width of the rectangle is $\dfrac{2}{5}$ cm, what is its length, $x$ cm? Give your answer in its simplest form.

> **Hint**
> This question combines fractions and geometry. Work out the area of the triangle. What is the same about both shapes?

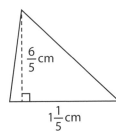

.................................................................. cm   [ ___ / 3 marks]

11

# Calculating with fractions 2

**1.** Work out and simplify where possible

    **a)** $\dfrac{1}{3}+\dfrac{1}{5}$

.................................................................. **[I got ___ / 2 marks]**

    **b)** $\dfrac{2}{9}+\dfrac{5}{6}$

.................................................................. **[ ___ / 2 marks]**

    **c)** $1\dfrac{7}{8}+2\dfrac{3}{4}$

.................................................................. **[ ___ / 3 marks]**

**2.** Work out and simplify where possible

    **a)** $\dfrac{7}{9}-\dfrac{1}{2}$

.................................................................. **[ ___ / 2 marks]**

    **b)** $3\dfrac{1}{6}-2\dfrac{3}{4}$

.................................................................. **[ ___ / 3 marks]**

**3.** Janet says that $\dfrac{2}{5}+\dfrac{4}{5}=\dfrac{6}{10}$. Is Janet correct? Give a reason for your answer.

..................................................................................................

..................................................................................................

.................................................................. **[ ___ / 1 mark]**

**4.** $\dfrac{1}{8}$ of the students in a class drive to school. $\dfrac{2}{3}$ of the students walk to school. The rest take the bus. Work out the fraction of students who take the bus.

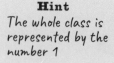

**Hint**
*The whole class is represented by the number 1*

.................................................................. **[ ___ / 3 marks]**

**5.** Daisy is building a model train track. Her track is $2\dfrac{4}{5}$m long. She then takes out a piece of track which is $\dfrac{7}{8}$m long and replaces it with a piece which is $1\dfrac{1}{20}$m long. Work out the length of her track now.

.................................................................. m   **[ ___ / 3 marks]**

**6.** Maxwell is reading a book on his e-reader. He is $\dfrac{1}{3}$ of the way through the book. When he puts it down he is $\dfrac{3}{4}$ of the way through the book. What fraction of the book did he read?

.................................................................. **[ ___ / 2 marks]**

# Fractions, decimals, percentages

**Grade 2**

**1. a)** Write 0.4 as a fraction in its simplest form.

.......................................................... [I got ___ / 1 mark]

**b)** Write 6% as a decimal.

.......................................................... [ ___ / 1 mark]

**c)** Write $\frac{1}{8}$ as a percentage.

.......................................................... [ ___ / 1 mark]

**Grade 2**

**2. a)** Convert $\frac{6}{5}$ to a percentage. Cirlce your answer.

     65%         12%         120%         650%      [ ___ / 1 mark]

**b)** Convert 0.035 to a fraction in its simplest form.

.......................................................... [ ___ / 1 mark]

**c)** Convert 3.6% to a decimal.

.......................................................... [ ___ / 1 mark]

**Grade 3**

**3.** Write these numbers in order of size, starting with the smallest.

     34%         0.3         $\frac{1}{3}$         $\frac{16}{50}$

.......................................................... [ ___ / 3 marks]

**Grade 3**

**4.** An online music streaming service, Dittify, does some research and finds that $\frac{7}{20}$ of its users listen to its daily mix playlist in the morning, $\frac{1}{5}$ of users listen to their own mix playlist and the rest choose an album.

Work out the percentage of users who choose an album.

> **Hint**
> Convert the fractions to percentages first.

.......................................................... [ ___ / 3 marks]

**Grade 4**

**5.** In Lin's class, 6 out of 25 students read fantasy books. In Jay's class, 8 out of 32 students read fantasy books. Lin says the proportion of students who read fantasy books is greater in her class than in Jay's. Is Lin correct? Give a reason for your answer.

..........................................................

.......................................................... [ ___ / 2 marks]

# Powers and roots

**1.** Write down the value of

**a)** $4^2$

...................................................................................... **[I got ___ / 1 mark]**

**b)** $2^3$

...................................................................................... **[ ___ / 1 mark]**

**c)** $\sqrt{49}$

...................................................................................... **[ ___ / 1 mark]**

**d)** $\sqrt[3]{27}$

...................................................................................... **[ ___ / 1 mark]**

**2.** Work out

**a)** $2 \times \sqrt{9 + 16} + 6^2$

...................................................................................... **[ ___ / 3 marks]**

**b)** $3^4 - 6 \times \sqrt[3]{8} + 50 \div 5^2$

...................................................................................... **[ ___ / 3 marks]**

**3.** The area of a square is 121 cm². Work out its perimeter.

121 cm²

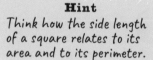
**Hint**
Think how the side length of a square relates to its area and to its perimeter.

...................................................................... cm **[ ___ / 2 marks]**

**4. a)** Using your calculator, work out the value of $\dfrac{\sqrt[3]{3.6^2} + 91 \times 3.7}{\sqrt{6.25} + 1.8^3}$

**Hint**
Remind yourself how to round to 3 sf.

Write down all the figures on your calculator display.

...................................................................................... **[ ___ / 1 mark]**

**b)** Write your answer to part **a** to 3 significant figures.

...................................................................................... **[ ___ / 1 mark]**

**5.** A cube-shaped box of side length 8 cm is made of solid metal. Work out how many smaller cubes of side length 2 cm will fill the box completely.

**Hint**
Consider the volume of the box and the volume of the smaller cubes.

...................................................................................... **[ ___ / 3 marks]**

# Calculating with indices

**Grade 4**

**1.** Simplify $7^2 \times 7^5$. Circle your answer.

**Hint**
*Remind yourself of the rules of indices.*

$7^{10}$        $14^7$        $49^7$        $7^7$        **[I got __ / 1 mark]**

**Grade 4**

**2.** Simplify

**a)** $9^{10} \div 9^4$

..................................................................... **[ __ / 1 mark]**

**b)** $2^5 \times 2^{-3}$

..................................................................... **[ __ / 1 mark]**

**c)** $7^{-2} \div 7^{-6}$

..................................................................... **[ __ / 1 mark]**

**d)** $(3^4)^4$

..................................................................... **[ __ / 1 mark]**

**Grade 4**

**3.** Simplify

**a)** $(8^2)^{-5}$

..................................................................... **[ __ / 1 mark]**

**b)** $\dfrac{9^3}{9^2 \times 9^4}$

..................................................................... **[ __ / 2 marks]**

**c)** $(2^7 \times 2^4)^{-1}$

..................................................................... **[ __ / 2 marks]**

**Grade 4**

**4.** Work out the area of the rectangle, leaving your answer in simplified index form.

$10^3$ cm

$10^2$ cm

........................................................ cm$^2$ **[ __ / 2 marks]**

**Grade 4**

**5.** Peter says that $2^3 \times 5^2$ simplifies to $10^5$. Give a reason why Peter is wrong.

..................................................................... **[ __ / 1 mark]**

**Grade 5**

**6.** Work out

**a)** $13^0$

..................................................................... **[ __ / 1 mark]**

**b)** $8^{-1}$

..................................................................... **[ __ / 1 mark]**

**c)** $\left(\dfrac{2}{5}\right)^3$

..................................................................... **[ __ / 1 mark]**

**d)** $\left(\dfrac{1}{4}\right)^{-2}$

..................................................................... **[ __ / 2 marks]**

15

# Factors and multiples

**Grade 2**

1. Here is a list of numbers.

3     6     8     10     18     24     30     36

Write down

a) a factor of 12

.................................................................................... **[I got ___ / 1 mark]**

b) a multiple of 9

.................................................................................... **[ ___ / 1 mark]**

c) a number which is both a multiple of 12 and a multiple of 4

.................................................................................... **[ ___ / 1 mark]**

d) a number which is both a factor of 24 and a factor of 16

.................................................................................... **[ ___ / 1 mark]**

e) two numbers with a common factor of 5

.................................................................................... **[ ___ / 1 mark]**

f) two numbers with a common multiple of 60

.................................................................................... **[ ___ / 1 mark]**

**Grade 3**

2. What is the lowest common multiple of 9 and 12? Circle your answer.

18      24      36      72 **[ ___ / 1 mark]**

**Grade 3**

3. What is the highest common factor of 18 and 12?

.................................................................................... **[ ___ / 2 marks]**

**Grade 4**

4. Three alarms beep at the same time. The first alarm then beeps every 6 minutes, the second then beeps every 5 minutes and the third beeps every 15 minutes. Work out how long it is before all three alarms beep at the same time.

> **Hint**
> Is this an HCF or an LCM question?

.............................................. minutes **[ ___ / 2 marks]**

**Grade 4**

5. Two 2-digit numbers have a highest common factor of 4 and a lowest common multiple of 60. What are the two numbers?

> **Hint**
> Remind yourself how to use prime factors to find the HCF and LCM.

.................................................................................... **[ ___ / 2 marks]**

# Prime factor decomposition

Grade 4 **1.** Write 110 as a product of its prime factors.

...................................................... **[I got ___ / 2 marks]**

Grade 4 **2. a)** Write 540 as a product of powers of its prime factors.

...................................................... **[ ___ / 2 marks]**

**b)** By looking at its prime factors, give a reason why 540 is divisible by 15

> **Hint**
> What are the prime factors of 15?

...................................................... **[ ___ / 1 mark]**

Grade 4 **3. a)** Write 750 as a product of its prime factors. Give your answer in index notation.

...................................................... **[ ___ / 2 marks]**

**b)** By looking at its prime factors, give a reason why 750 is not divisible by 4

...................................................... **[ ___ / 1 mark]**

Grade 5 **4.** The prime factor decomposition of a number, $x$, is $2 \times 3^2 \times 7 \times 13$

**a)** Is $x$ even or odd? Give your reasoning.

...................................................... **[ ___ / 1 mark]**

**b)** What is the prime factor decomposition of a number twice as big as $x$?

...................................................... **[ ___ / 1 mark]**

Grade 5 **5.** A number is a multiple of 4, 5 and 6. Write the prime factor decomposition of the smallest number it could be.

...................................................... **[ ___ / 2 marks]**

# Finding HCF and LCM

**1. a)** Circle 160 as a product of prime factors.

$$2 \times 4^2 \times 5 \qquad 2^4 \times 5^2 \qquad 4^2 \times 5^2 \qquad 2^5 \times 5$$

**[I got ___ / 1 mark]**

**b)** Work out the highest common factor of 160 and 280

...................................................................................... **[ ___ / 2 marks]**

**c)** Work out the lowest common multiple of 160 and 280

...................................................................................... **[ ___ / 2 marks]**

**2.** Two numbers have prime factor decompositions $2^3 \times 5 \times 11$ and $2 \times 3^2 \times 5$

Work out

> **Hint**
> You may wish to use a Venn diagram to help with this question.

**a)** the highest common factor of the two numbers

...................................................................................... **[ ___ / 2 marks]**

**b)** the lowest common multiple of the two numbers.

...................................................................................... **[ ___ / 1 mark]**

**3.** Fran is sorting her books into piles. She has 225 yellow books and 324 orange books. She does not want to mix the colours and wants every pile to contain the same number of books. Work out the biggest number of books she can put in each pile.

...................................................................................... **[ ___ / 3 marks]**

# Standard form

**Grade 3**

**1.** Write $1.56 \times 10^8$ as an ordinary number.

.................................................................... **[I got __ / 1 mark]**

**Grade 3**

**2.** Circle the ordinary form of the number $8.02 \times 10^{-3}$

0.00802          0.0802          8020          802000

**[ __ / 1 mark]**

**Grade 3**

**3.** Write these numbers in standard form.

**a)** 48 000 000 000

.................................................................... **[ __ / 1 mark]**

**b)** 0.000 0703

.................................................................... **[ __ / 1 mark]**

**c)** $95 \times 10^6$

.................................................................... **[ __ / 1 mark]**

**d)** $0.68 \times 10^{-4}$

.................................................................... **[ __ / 1 mark]**

**Grade 3**

**4.** The distance from the Sun to Earth is approximately 150 000 000 km.
Write this number in standard form.

.................................................... km    **[ __ / 1 mark]**

**Grade 4**

**5.** Put these numbers in order of size, starting with the biggest.

$2.1 \times 10^4$        $2.3 \times 10^5$        $0.21 \times 10^4$        2200

**Hint**
*Write all the numbers in the same form.*

.................................................................... **[ __ / 3 marks]**

**Grade 4**

**6.** The size of a bacteria cell is $4 \times 10^{-7}$ m and the size of a virus is 0.000 000 05 m.
Which is smaller, the bacteria cell or the virus?

.................................................................... **[ __ / 2 marks]**

# Calculating with standard form

**1.** Work out the value of each expression, giving your answers in standard form.

**a)** $2 \times (3 \times 10^2)$

[I got ___ / 1 mark]

**b)** $(4 \times 10^{-4}) \div 2$

[ ___ / 1 mark]

**c)** $(3 \times 10^{-2}) + (5 \times 10^{-2})$

[ ___ / 1 mark]

**d)** $(9 \times 10^7) - (3 \times 10^7)$

[ ___ / 1 mark]

**2.** Everly says that $6 \times (3 \times 10^6)$ is written as $18 \times 10^6$ in standard form.

Is Everly correct? Give your reasoning.

[ ___ / 1 mark]

**3.** Work out the value of $7 \times 10^{-2} \times 30\,000$. Circle your answer.

$21 \times 10^2$       $10 \times 10^2$       $2.1 \times 10^3$       $2.1 \times 10^{-8}$

[ ___ / 1 mark]

**4.** Work out the value of each expression, giving your answers in standard form.

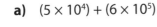

**a)** $(5 \times 10^4) + (6 \times 10^5)$

[ ___ / 2 marks]

**b)** $(9 \times 10^{-3}) - (3 \times 10^{-4})$

[ ___ / 2 marks]

**c)** $(2.1 \times 10^8) \times (3 \times 10^{-5})$

[ ___ / 2 marks]

**d)** $(8.2 \times 10^3) \div (4.1 \times 10^7)$

[ ___ / 2 marks]

# Terms and expressions

**1.** James is $n$ years old. Lily is two years younger than James. Katie is eleven years older than Lily.

   **a)** Circle the expression for Lily's age.

$$n + 2 \qquad 2 - n \qquad 2 + n \qquad n - 2$$

**[I got ___ / 1 mark]**

   **b)** Write an expression for Katie's age.

........................................................................ **[ ___ / 1 mark]**

**2.** Rossi has $g$ games on his console. Nisha has three times as many games as Rossi. Write an expression for the number of games Nisha has.

........................................................................ **[ ___ / 1 mark]**

**3.** In a shop, football cards cost £2 per pack and athletics cards cost £3 per pack. Theo buys $x$ packs of football cards and $y$ packs of athletics cards. Write an expression for the total cost of the cards.

£........................................................................ **[ ___ / 2 marks]**

**4.** Write an expression for the perimeter of this triangle.

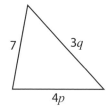

........................................................................ **[ ___ / 1 mark]**

**5.** Work out the value of each of these expressions when $a = 5$, $b = 2$ and $c = -4$

   **a)** $2a + 3b$

........................................................................ **[ ___ / 2 marks]**

   **b)** $10 - c$

........................................................................ **[ ___ / 2 marks]**

   **c)** $\dfrac{8a}{c}$

........................................................................ **[ ___ / 2 marks]**

   **d)** $ac + b$

........................................................................ **[ ___ / 2 marks]**

# Simplifying expressions

**1.** Simplify

    **a)** $2x + 3x - x$

...................................................................................................... [I got ___ / 1 mark]

    **b)** $3p - 5q + 7q - 2q + 4p$

...................................................................................................... [ ___ / 2 marks]

    **c)** $7 + 5t - 2 - 9t$

...................................................................................................... [ ___ / 2 marks]

**2.** Simplify

    **a)** $x^2 + 4x + 3x^2 - 6x + 1$

...................................................................................................... [ ___ / 2 marks]

    **b)** $9mn - 2m^2 + 7nm + 11m^2$

...................................................................................................... [ ___ / 2 marks]

**3.** Write an expression for the perimeter of this quadrilateral.

Give your answer in its simplest form.

> **Hint**
> The perimeter is the distance around the edges of the shape.

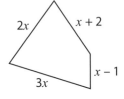

...................................................................................................... [ ___ / 2 marks]

**4.** Write an expression for the area of this L-shape. Give your answer in its simplest form.

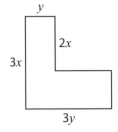

...................................................................................................... [ ___ / 3 marks]

**5.** Nikita has $x$ toys. Gabriella has twice as many as Nikita. Paulo has three more than Nikita and Gabriella put together. Write an expression for the number of toys the three children have in total. Give your answer in its simplest form.

...................................................................................................... [ ___ / 3 marks]

# Formulae

**1.** To work out the cost, in pounds, of a piano repair, a technician uses the formula

Cost = 80 + number of hours worked × 15

**a)** Work out the cost of a repair that takes the technician 5 hours.

£................................................................ **[I got ___ / 2 marks]**

**b)** A repair costs £275. How many hours did it take?

................................................................ hours **[ ___ / 2 marks]**

**2.** For each formula, work out the value of $d$ when $c = 4$

**a)** $d = \dfrac{c + 5}{2}$

................................................................ **[ ___ / 2 marks]**

**b)** $d = c^2 - 3c$

................................................................ **[ ___ / 2 marks]**

**c)** $c = 2d - 12$

**Hint**
You may need to work backwards here.

................................................................ **[ ___ / 3 marks]**

**3.** The acceleration, $a$, of a car is given by the formula $a = \dfrac{v - u}{t}$, where $u$ is its starting speed, $v$ is its ending speed, and $t$ is the time it has been travelling for. Work out the acceleration of a car that goes from 0 m/s to 24 m/s in 8 seconds.

................................................................ m/s² **[ ___ / 2 marks]**

**4.** Raj is putting on a children's party. The room costs £100 to hire. A bouncy castle costs £40 per hour to hire. Write a formula for the cost, £$C$, of hiring the room and a bouncy castle for $t$ hours.

................................................................ **[ ___ / 2 marks]**

**5.** To work out the number of tablets to give a patient, a nurse uses the formula

Number of tablets = $\dfrac{D}{S}$

where $D$ is the required dose and $S$ is the dose in each tablet. A nurse is required to give a dose of 17.5 mg and each tablet contains 3.5 mg. How many tablets should the nurse give?

................................................................ **[ ___ / 2 marks]**

# Equations and identities

**1.** For each part, identify whether it is an expression, formula, equation or identity. Complete the table. The first one has been done for you.

a) $2x + 3 = 5$

b) $S = \left(\dfrac{u + v}{2}\right)t$

c) $x^2 = 9$

d) $3x + 5x - 2x = 6x$

e) $4k - 2$

f) $V = IR$

g) $y^2 - 9y + 20$

h) $6p^2 - 4p + 2p^2 + 3p = 8p^2 - p$

| Expression | Formula | Equation | Identity |
|---|---|---|---|
|  |  | a) $2x + 3 = 5$ |  |

**[I got ___ / 7 marks]**

**2.** Write which of **A** to **F** are identities.

**A**  $x + x + 3 = 3 + 2x$

**B**  $4y - 3 = 2y$

**C**  $a - b = b - a$

**D**  $m - n = -n + m$

**E**  $4x + 3 - 2y + 1 = 4x - 2y + 4$

**F**  $m + 2 = m + 3$

> **Hint**
> If the left-hand side can be simplified or rewritten to match the right, it is an identity.

**[ ___ / 3 marks]**

**3.** Seb says that $5x - 2 \equiv 3x$. Is Seb correct? Give a reason for your answer.

**[ ___ / 1 mark]**

# Functions

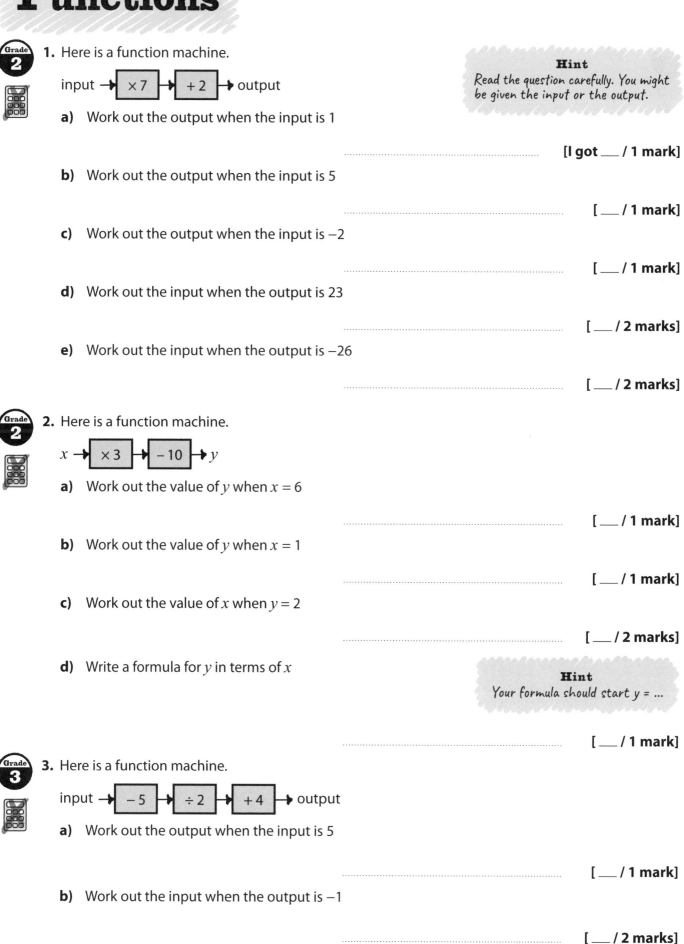

**Grade 2**

**1.** Here is a function machine.

input → ×7 → +2 → output

**a)** Work out the output when the input is 1

............................................................ **[I got ___ / 1 mark]**

**Hint**
Read the question carefully. You might
be given the input or the output.

**b)** Work out the output when the input is 5

............................................................ **[ ___ / 1 mark]**

**c)** Work out the output when the input is −2

............................................................ **[ ___ / 1 mark]**

**d)** Work out the input when the output is 23

............................................................ **[ ___ / 2 marks]**

**e)** Work out the input when the output is −26

............................................................ **[ ___ / 2 marks]**

**Grade 2**

**2.** Here is a function machine.

$x$ → ×3 → −10 → $y$

**a)** Work out the value of $y$ when $x = 6$

............................................................ **[ ___ / 1 mark]**

**b)** Work out the value of $y$ when $x = 1$

............................................................ **[ ___ / 1 mark]**

**c)** Work out the value of $x$ when $y = 2$

............................................................ **[ ___ / 2 marks]**

**d)** Write a formula for $y$ in terms of $x$

**Hint**
Your formula should start y = ...

............................................................ **[ ___ / 1 mark]**

**Grade 3**

**3.** Here is a function machine.

input → −5 → ÷2 → +4 → output

**a)** Work out the output when the input is 5

............................................................ **[ ___ / 1 mark]**

**b)** Work out the input when the output is −1

............................................................ **[ ___ / 2 marks]**

**c)** Write the output when the input is $h$

............................................................ **[ ___ / 2 marks]**

# Solving linear equations

**1.** Solve

    **a)** $4t = 28$

    ................................................................ **[I got ___ / 1 mark]**

    **b)** $w + 6 = 15$

    ................................................................ **[ ___ / 1 mark]**

    **c)** $15 - p = 8$

    ................................................................ **[ ___ / 1 mark]**

    **d)** $\dfrac{b}{5} = 10$

    ................................................................ **[ ___ / 1 mark]**

**2.** Solve

    **a)** $2x + 4 = 9$

    ................................................................ **[ ___ / 2 marks]**

    **b)** $19 = 3y - 2$

    ................................................................ **[ ___ / 2 marks]**

    **c)** $-4 = 5q + 6$

    ................................................................ **[ ___ / 2 marks]**

**3.** The perimeter of the kite is 38 cm.

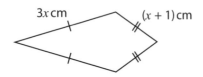

    **a)** Circle the correct expression for the perimeter of the kite in terms of $x$

        $4x + 1$          $8x + 2$          $5x$          $10x$          **[ ___ / 1 mark]**

    **b)** Find the value of $x$

    ................................................................ **[ ___ / 2 marks]**

**4.** In a golf game, Sarah plays $n$ holes, Ewan plays five fewer than Sarah and Cameron plays twice as many as Sarah. If they play 35 holes in total, form and solve an equation to work out how many holes Sarah plays.

    ................................................................ **[ ___ / 3 marks]**

# Harder linear equations

**1.** Solve

a) $\dfrac{a}{4} - 1 = 10$

..................................................... **[I got ___ / 2 marks]**

b) $11 = 2 + \dfrac{c}{3}$

..................................................... **[ ___ / 2 marks]**

c) $\dfrac{f - 5}{4} = 10$

..................................................... **[ ___ / 2 marks]**

**2.** Solve

a) $\dfrac{2k + 1}{3} = -4$

..................................................... **[ ___ / 2 marks]**

b) $5p + 3 = 3p + 7$

..................................................... **[ ___ / 2 marks]**

c) $3 + p = 4p - 6$

..................................................... **[ ___ / 2 marks]**

d) $9 - 6p = 4 - 11p$

..................................................... **[ ___ / 2 marks]**

**3.** Rosalind thinks of a number. She multiplies her number by two, adds three and then writes the answer. Next, she multiplies her original number by three, subtracts four and writes the answer. Rosalind realises she has written the same answer both times. What is Rosalind's number?

> **Hint**
> Form and solve an equation using
> x for the unknown number.

..................................................... **[ ___ / 3 marks]**

**4.** This shape is a rectangle.

a) Form and solve an equation to work out the value of $x$

..................................................... **[ ___ / 3 marks]**

b) If the perimeter of the rectangle is 34 cm, work out the area of the rectangle.

..................................................... cm² **[ ___ / 4 marks]**

# Rearranging formulae

**1.** Rearrange each of the formulae to make $p$ the subject.

   **a)**   $q = p + 3r$

   .................................................................................... **[I got ___ / 1 mark]**

   **b)**   $r = 3p + 2$

   .................................................................................... **[ ___ / 2 marks]**

   **c)**   $q = p^2$

   .................................................................................... **[ ___ / 1 mark]**

   **d)**   $\dfrac{q + p}{6} = r$

   .................................................................................... **[ ___ / 2 marks]**

**2.** Make $x$ the subject of the formulae.

   **a)**   $2x^2 - 3 = y$

   .................................................................................... **[ ___ / 2 marks]**

   **b)**   $a\sqrt{x} + b = c$

   .................................................................................... **[ ___ / 2 marks]**

**3.** The power, $p$ watts, in a circuit is given by the formula

$$p = I^2 R$$

   where $I$ is the current in amps and $R$ is the resistance in ohms.
   Rearrange the formula to make $I$ the subject.

> **Hint**
> Think carefully about what
> is happening to $I$

   .................................................................................... **[ ___ / 2 marks]**

**4.** Fleur is rearranging a formula to make $x$ the subject. Her steps are shown. Give a criticism of Fleur's
   working.

$$\begin{array}{l} y = a^2 x - b \\ y + b = a^2 x \\ \sqrt{y + b} = ax \\ \dfrac{\sqrt{y + b}}{a} = x \end{array}$$

   ....................................................................

   ....................................................................

   .................................................................... **[ ___ / 2 marks]**

# Expanding single brackets

**1.** Expand

   **a)** $5(x + 3)$

........................................................................ **[I got ___ / 1 mark]**

   **b)** $a(x - 2)$

........................................................................ **[ ___ / 2 marks]**

   **c)** $2x(3x - y)$

........................................................................ **[ ___ / 2 marks]**

   **d)** $(5x - 1)x$

........................................................................ **[ ___ / 2 marks]**

**2.** Expand and simplify fully

   **a)** $2(x + 4) + 3(x - 8)$

> **Hint**
> Expand each bracket separately and be careful when subtracting.

........................................................................ **[ ___ / 3 marks]**

   **b)** $9(x + 2) - 4(2x - 1)$

........................................................................ **[ ___ / 3 marks]**

   **c)** $4(y + 3) - (y + 2)$

........................................................................ **[ ___ / 3 marks]**

**3. a)** Write an expression for the area of this triangle.

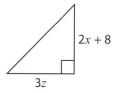

........................................................................ **[ ___ / 2 marks]**

   **b)** Expand your expression in part **a**.

........................................................................ **[ ___ / 1 mark]**

**4.** Graham states that the difference in area between the square and the rectangle is $7x^2 + 8x$. Show that Graham is correct.

> **Hint**
> Work out expressions for the areas of the shapes.

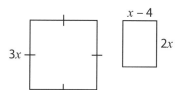

........................................................................ **[ ___ / 3 marks]**

# Factorising into single brackets

**Grade 4** **1.** Factorise

    **a)** $4x + 6y$

    .................................................. **[I got __ / 1 mark]**

    **b)** $10x - 5y$

    .................................................. **[ __ / 1 mark]**

    **c)** $pq - 2p$

    .................................................. **[ __ / 1 mark]**

**Grade 4** **2.** Factorise $12a + 30b$ fully. Circle your answer.

    $2(6a + 15b)$      $12(a + 18b)$      $6(2a + 5b)$      $(4a + 10b)$      **[ __ / 1 mark]**

**Grade 4** **3.** Factorise fully

    **a)** $20x^2 - 5x$

> **Hint**
> When you're told to factorise 'fully', make sure you take the highest common factor out of the brackets.

    .................................................. **[ __ / 2 marks]**

    **b)** $8pq - 6p^2$

    .................................................. **[ __ / 2 marks]**

    **c)** $5yz - 20y$

    .................................................. **[ __ / 2 marks]**

    **d)** $16x + 12xy$

    .................................................. **[ __ / 2 marks]**

    **e)** $x^2y + y^2x$

    .................................................. **[ __ / 2 marks]**

    **f)** $8p - 4p^2q + 6pq$

    .................................................. **[ __ / 2 marks]**

**Grade 5** **4.** Work out the missing length on the diagram. The area is given as $x^2 + 3x$

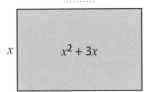

    .................................................. **[ __ / 1 mark]**

**Grade 5** **5.** The area of a rectangle is $4xz + 10xyz$. Write a possible length and width of the rectangle.

    .................................................. **[ __ / 2 marks]**

# Expanding double brackets

**1.** Expand and simplify

   **a)** $(x + 5)(x + 7)$

......................................................................... **[I got __ / 2 marks]**

   **b)** $(m - 3)(m + 4)$

......................................................................... **[ __ / 2 marks]**

   **c)** $(y - 5)(y - 4)$

......................................................................... **[ __ / 2 marks]**

   **d)** $(x + 3)^2$

......................................................................... **[ __ / 2 marks]**

**2.** Expand $(y - 8)^2$. Circle your answer.

   $y^2 + 64$         $y^2 - 16y - 64$         $y^2 - 16y + 64$         $y^2 - 64$         **[ __ / 1 mark]**

**3.** Expand and simplify if possible

   **a)** $(x + 2)(y + 1)$

......................................................................... **[ __ / 2 marks]**

   **b)** $(2a - 5)(2 + a)$

......................................................................... **[ __ / 2 marks]**

   **c)** $(a + b)^2$

......................................................................... **[ __ / 2 marks]**

   **d)** $(2m + 3n)(3m - 2n)$

......................................................................... **[ __ / 2 marks]**

   **e)** $(4x + 1)^2$

......................................................................... **[ __ / 2 marks]**

**4.** Work out an expression for the area of the triangle.
   Give your answer in expanded form.

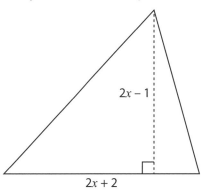

> **Hint**
> Here, algebra is combined with geometry. Remember the formula:
> Area of a triangle = $\frac{1}{2}$ × base × height

......................................................................... **[ __ / 3 marks]**

**31**

# Factorising into double brackets

**1.** Factorise

    **a)** $x^2 + 5x + 6$

.................................................................. **[I got ___ / 2 marks]**

    **b)** $y^2 - 3y + 2$

.................................................................. **[ ___ / 2 marks]**

    **c)** $p^2 - 9p - 36$

.................................................................. **[ ___ / 2 marks]**

    **d)** $x^2 + 9x - 10$

.................................................................. **[ ___ / 2 marks]**

    **e)** $y^2 - 14y + 49$

.................................................................. **[ ___ / 2 marks]**

    **f)** $x^2 + 8x + 16$

.................................................................. **[ ___ / 2 marks]**

**2.** A rectangle has area $x^2 + 6x - 27$. Work out expressions for the lengths of the two sides of the rectangle.

$$x^2 + 6x - 27$$

> **Hint**
> When you factorise, you get two expressions that multiply to make the given one. How does this link to the area of a rectangle?

.................................................................. **[ ___ / 2 marks]**

**3.** Pavel says that $x^2 + 5x - 6$ factorises to $(x + 2)(x + 3)$ since the sum of 2 and 3 is 5 and the product of 2 and 3 is 6. Give a reason why Pavel is wrong.

.................................................................. **[ ___ / 1 mark]**

**4.** A square has area $x^2 + 6x + 9$. Work out the perimeter of the square in terms of $x$.

.................................................................. **[ ___ / 3 marks]**

# Difference of two squares

 **1.** Expand

    **a)** $(x - 2)(x + 2)$

.................................................... **[I got ___ / 2 marks]**

    **b)** $(y + 10)(y - 10)$

.................................................... **[ ___ / 2 marks]**

    **c)** $(p - 3)(p + 3)$

.................................................... **[ ___ / 2 marks]**

 **2.** Factorise fully

    **a)** $x^2 - 49$

.................................................... **[ ___ / 1 mark]**

    **b)** $y^2 - 81$

.................................................... **[ ___ / 1 mark]**

    **c)** $b^2 - 121$

.................................................... **[ ___ / 1 mark]**

    **d)** $p^2 - 9q^2$

.................................................... **[ ___ / 1 mark]**

 **3.** Factorise fully

    **a)** $y^2 + 16y$

> **Hint**
> *Not all of these are the difference of two squares.*

.................................................... **[ ___ / 1 mark]**

    **b)** $x^2 - 16$

.................................................... **[ ___ / 1 mark]**

    **c)** $a^2 + 16a + 64$

.................................................... **[ ___ / 2 marks]**

    **d)** $q^2 - 16q + 60$

.................................................... **[ ___ / 2 marks]**

    **e)** $n^2 - 144$

.................................................... **[ ___ / 1 mark]**

 **4.** The area of a parallelogram is $x^2 - 121$. Write expressions for the base and height of the parallelogram in terms of $x$.

$x^2 - 121$

.................................................... **[ ___ / 2 marks]**

# Solving quadratic equations

Grade 5

**1.** Solve

    **a)** $x^2 + 9x + 20 = 0$

............................................... **[I got ___ / 3 marks]**

    **b)** $x^2 - 7x - 8 = 0$

............................................... **[ ___ / 3 marks]**

    **c)** $x^2 + 5x = 0$

............................................... **[ ___ / 3 marks]**

    **d)** $x^2 - 1 = 0$

............................................... **[ ___ / 3 marks]**

Grade 5

**2.** Solve

    **a)** $2x^2 + 6x = 0$

> **Hint**
> Before solving, make sure
> one side of the equation is 0

............................................... **[ ___ / 3 marks]**

    **b)** $x^2 - 12x = -35$

............................................... **[ ___ / 4 marks]**

    **c)** $x^2 + 3x = 10$

............................................... **[ ___ / 4 marks]**

    **d)** $x^2 = 144$

............................................... **[ ___ / 2 marks]**

Grade 5

**3.** Here is a rectangle. The area of the rectangle is 12 cm².

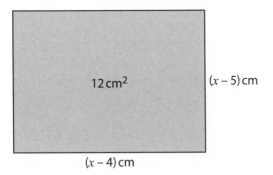

12 cm²   $(x-5)$ cm

$(x-4)$ cm

    **a)** Show that $x^2 - 9x + 8 = 0$

............................................... **[ ___ / 3 marks]**

    **b)** Work out the length of the shortest side of the rectangle.

............................................... cm    **[ ___ / 3 marks]**

# Simultaneous equations 1

*x + y's are variables*

**1.** Solve each pair of simultaneous equations.

**a)**  $x + y = 14$

$x - y = 8$

.................................................................... **[I got ___ / 2 marks]**

**b)** 1) $2x - 2y = 4$

2) $2x + 3y = 14$   +

$\underline{\phantom{xx}}$

$4x + 5y = 18$

$2x + 3y = 14$  $-$

$\underline{2x - 2y = 4}$  $-$

$x + 1y = 10$

$x = 9$

$2x - 2y = 4$

$9 - 2y = 4$

$y = 5$

$x = 9$    $y = 5$

.................................................................... **[___ / 3 marks]**

**c)** 1) $4x + 5y = 37$

2) $2x + y = 11$

$\cancel{x \sim \sim 5x}$

.................................................................... **[___ / 3 marks]**

**d)**  $3x - 2y = 2$

$12x - 4y = 10$

.................................................................... **[___ / 3 marks]**

**2.** Solve each pair of simultaneous equations.

**a)**  $2x + 5y = 11$

$3x - 2y = -12$

> **Hint**
> You might have to change both equations to make the coefficients of $x$ or $y$ match.

.................................................................... **[___ / 3 marks]**

**b)**  $2x - 7y = 12$

$5x - y = -3$

.................................................................... **[___ / 3 marks]**

**c)**  $3x + 8y = 12$

$2x + 12y = 13$

.................................................................... **[___ / 3 marks]**

**d)**  $6x - 4y = 9$

$5x + 3y = -2$

.................................................................... **[___ / 3 marks]**

**35**

# Simultaneous equations 2

**1.** Two families go to the cinema. The first family buys one adult ticket and three child tickets and pays £39. The second family buys two adult tickets and four child tickets and pays £62.

   **a)** Form a pair of simultaneous equations to describe this situation.

   ............................................................................................................... **[I got ___ / 2 marks]**

   **b)** Solve your equations to work out the cost of an adult ticket and the cost of a child ticket.

   ............................................................................................ **[ ___ / 3 marks]**

**2.** The mass of 20 apples and 30 satsumas is 4050 g. The mass of 12 apples and 15 satsumas is 2205 g.

   Work out the mass of one apple and the mass of one satsuma.

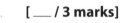

> **Hint**
> If you have two bits of information about two unknowns, write two simultaneous equations.

   ............................................................................................ **[ ___ / 4 marks]**

**3.** In the diagram, a square has area $x$ cm² and a rectangle has area $y$ cm².

   The total area of shape $A$ is 108 cm².

   The total area of shape $B$ is 128 cm².

   Work out the area of a square and the area of a rectangle.

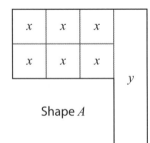

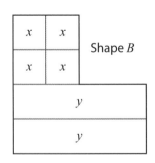

   ............................................................................................ **[ ___ / 4 marks]**

# Solving inequalities

**1.** Show the inequalities on the number lines.

a) $x > 7$

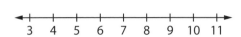

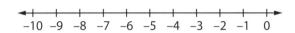

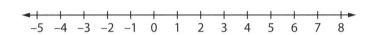

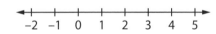

*Hint*
Remember to show if an end point on a number line is included in the inequality.

**[I got ___ / 1 mark]**

b) $x \leq -4$

**[ ___ / 1 mark]**

c) $-2 \leq x < 5$

**[ ___ / 2 marks]**

d) $1 \leq x$

**[ ___ / 1 mark]**

**2.** $n$ is an integer and $-1 \leq n < 5$. List the possible values of $n$

**[ ___ / 1 mark]**

**3.** $n$ is an integer and $-6 < 2n \leq 8$. List the possible values of $n$

**[ ___ / 2 marks]**

**4.** Solve

a) $2x \geq 5$

**[ ___ / 2 marks]**

b) $2x - 1 < 5$

**[ ___ / 3 marks]**

c) $3x + 5 > 2$

**[ ___ / 3 marks]**

d) $20 - 5x \geq 0$

**[ ___ / 3 marks]**

# Drawing linear graphs

**1. a)** Complete the table of values for $y = 3x - 1$

| $x$ | −1 | 0 | 1 | 2 | 3 |
|---|---|---|---|---|---|
| $y$ | | | 2 | | 8 |

[I got ___ / 2 marks]

**b)** Draw the graph of $y = 3x - 1$ on the grid.

**Hint**
Use your ruler to draw a single straight line through all the points.

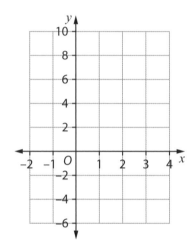

[ ___ / 2 marks]

**2. a)** Complete the table of values for $x + y = 5$

| $x$ | −2 | −1 | 0 | 1 | 2 |
|---|---|---|---|---|---|
| $y$ | | 6 | | 4 | |

[ ___ / 2 marks]

**b)** Draw the graph of $x + y = 5$ on the grid.

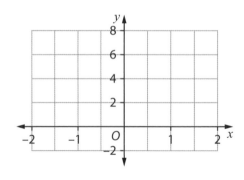

[ ___ / 2 marks]

**3.** On the grid, draw the graph of $y = 3 - 2x$

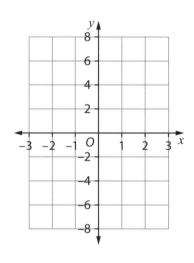

[ ___ / 3 marks]

# Working out gradients

**1.** Work out the gradient of each line segment.

a)

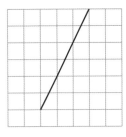

...........................

b)

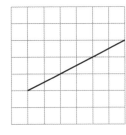

...........................

c)

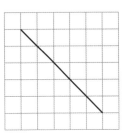

...........................

d)

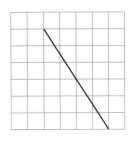

...........................

**[I got ___ / 8 marks]**

**2. a)** Work out the gradient of the line.

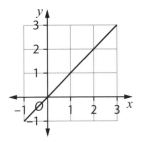

.......................................................................... **[ ___ / 2 marks]**

**b)** Write the equation of the line.

> **Hint**
> The equation of a line going through $(0, 0)$
> is $y = mx$ where $m$ is the gradient.

.......................................................................... **[ ___ / 1 mark]**

**3. a)** Work out the gradient of the line.

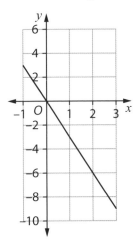

.......................................................................... **[ ___ / 2 marks]**

**b)** Write the equation of the line.

.......................................................................... **[ ___ / 1 mark]**

# Equation of a straight line

Grade 4

**1.** Work out the gradient and *y*-intercept of each of these lines.

> **Hint**
> You may need to rearrange the equation to make *y* the subject.

a) $y = 5x + 1$

Gradient .................................

*y*-intercept ................................. **[I got ___ / 2 marks]**

b) $y = 3 - 2x$

Gradient .................................

*y*-intercept ................................. **[ ___ / 2 marks]**

c) $2y = x + 6$

Gradient .................................

*y*-intercept ................................. **[ ___ / 3 marks]**

d) $y - x = 10$

Gradient .................................

*y*-intercept ................................. **[ ___ / 3 marks]**

e) $8x + 4y = 3$

Gradient .................................

*y*-intercept ................................. **[ ___ / 3 marks]**

Grade 4

**2.** Which of these lines is parallel to $y = 4x - 8$? Circle your answer.

$y = 3x - 8$     $y = -4x - 8$     $y = 3 - 4x$     $y = 4x + 3$     **[ ___ / 1 mark]**

Grade 5

**3.** Work out the equation of the line that passes through these two points.

a) (0, −1) and (2, 3)

................................................. **[ ___ / 3 marks]**

b) (−3, 5) and (1, 1)

................................................. **[ ___ / 3 marks]**

Grade 5

**4.** A line, *L*, has equation $y = 4 - 3x$. Sajid says that the line $3x + y = 0$ is parallel to *L*. Is Sajid correct? Give a reason for your answer.

...............................................................................................................

............................................... **[ ___ / 2 marks]**

# Kinematic graphs

1. Kai goes on a bike ride from home one day. Here is a travel graph showing part of Kai's bike ride.

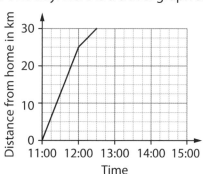

a) How far did Kai travel in the first hour and a half of his ride?

.................................................... km    **[I got ___ / 1 mark]**

b) Kai travelled at a slower speed after 12:00 than he did before 12:00. Give a reason why you know this.

.................................................................................................    **[ ___ / 1 mark]**

c) Work out Kai's speed, in km/h, for the 30 minutes after 12:00

> **Hint**
> How far would Kai travel in one hour?

.................................................... km/h    **[ ___ / 2 marks]**

d) At 12:30, Kai stops for lunch for 45 minutes before cycling back home at 20 km/h.
   Complete the travel graph.    **[ ___ / 2 marks]**

2. Here is a speed–time graph showing Krystyna's speeds for a 10 km race.

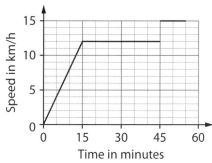

a) After how many minutes does Krystyna finish the race?

.................................................... minutes    **[ ___ / 1 mark]**

b) Write the time when Krystyna's speed is 8 km/h.

.................................................................    **[ ___ / 1 mark]**

c) Describe Krystyna's journey/speed during the race.

...............................................................................................................

...............................................................................................................    **[ ___ / 3 marks]**

# Quadratic graphs

**1. a)** Complete the table of values for the graph of $y = x^2 - x - 1$

| $x$ | −2 | −1 | 0 | 1 | 2 | 3 |
|---|---|---|---|---|---|---|
| $y$ | | 1 | | | | 5 |

**[I got ___ / 2 marks]**

**b)** Draw the graph of $y = x^2 - x - 1$

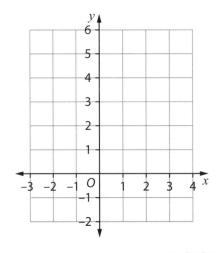

**[ ___ / 2 marks]**

**c)** Use your graph to estimate the coordinates of the turning point of the graph.

**Hint**
The turning point is the maximum or minimum.

............................................................ **[ ___ / 1 mark]**

**2.** Here is the graph of $y = 2 - x^2$

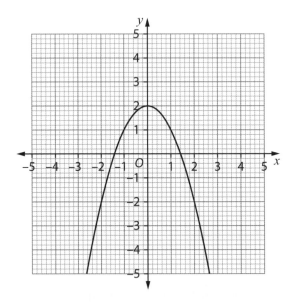

**a)** Use the graph to estimate the roots of $2 - x^2 = 0$

............................................................ **[ ___ / 2 marks]**

**b)** Write the coordinates of the turning point of $y = 2 - x^2$

............................................................ **[ ___ / 1 mark]**

**c)** Use your graph to estimate the values of $x$ for which $y = -3$

............................................................ **[ ___ / 2 marks]**

# Solutions from graphs

 **1.** The graphs of $y = 2x - 3$ and $x + y = 4$ are shown.

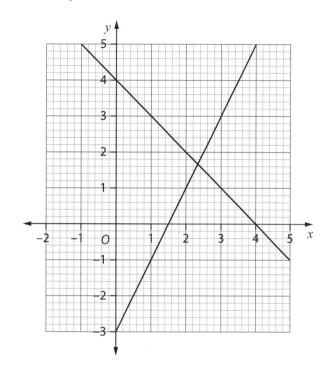

**Hint**
The solution of two simultaneous equations is where the lines intersect.

Use the graphs to estimate the solution to these simultaneous equations.

$$y = 2x - 3$$
$$x + y = 4$$

$x =$ ................................................. $\qquad$ $y =$ ................................................. **[I got ___ / 2 marks]**

 **2.** The graph of $x + 2y = 6$ is shown.

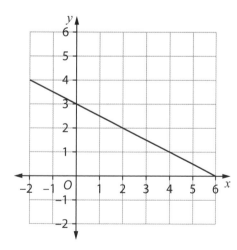

By drawing a suitable line on the graph, work out the solution to these simultaneous equations.

$$x + 2y = 6$$
$$y = x$$

$x =$ ................................................. $\qquad$ $y =$ ................................................. **[ ___ / 2 marks]**

# Cubic and reciprocal graphs

**1.** Match the graphs to their equations by completing the table.

**A**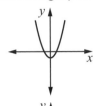

**B**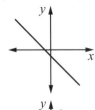

**C**

**D**

| Equation | Graph |
|---|---|
| $y = \dfrac{1}{x}$ | |
| $y = x^3 + 1$ | |
| $y = x^2 - 1$ | |
| $y = -x - 1$ | |

**[I got ___ / 3 marks]**

**2. a)** Complete the table of values for $y = x^3 - 1$

| $x$ | $-2$ | $-1$ | $0$ | $1$ | $2$ |
|---|---|---|---|---|---|
| $y$ | | $-2$ | $-1$ | | |

> **Hint**
> Follow BIDMAS when you work this out.

**[ ___ / 2 marks]**

**b)** Draw the graph of $y = x^3 - 1$

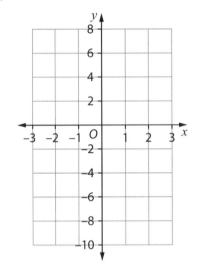

**[ ___ / 2 marks]**

**3. a)** Complete the table of values for $y = 2x^3 + 1$

| $x$ | $-2$ | $-1$ | $0$ | $1$ | $2$ |
|---|---|---|---|---|---|
| $y$ | $-15$ | | | | $17$ |

**[ ___ / 2 marks]**

**b)** Draw the graph of $y = 2x^3 + 1$

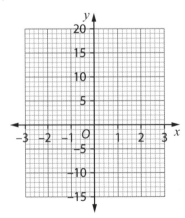

**[ ___ / 2 marks]**

**c)** Use your graph to estimate the root of $2x^3 + 1 = 0$

...................................................... **[ ___ / 1 mark]**

# Rates of change

**1.** David mows his lawn every few weeks. The graph shows the height of his lawn over a period of 12 weeks one summer.

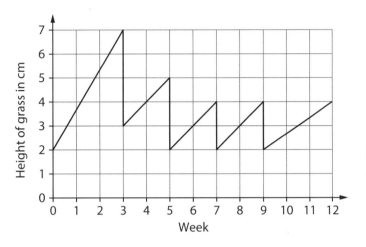

> **Hint**
> The steeper the graph, the faster the rate of change.

**a)** In which weeks does David cut the lawn?

.................................................... **[I got ___ / 1 mark]**

**b)** Between which weeks does the grass grow at the slowest rate?

.................................................... **[ ___ / 1 mark]**

**c)** What was the rate of growth of the grass, in cm/week, between weeks 5 and 7?

.................................................... cm/week **[ ___ / 1 mark]**

**2.** Here are the cross-sections of three swimming pools.

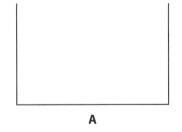      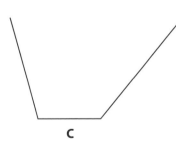

Each pool is filled with water from a hose. Match each pool to the correct graph showing the depth of water in the pool over time.

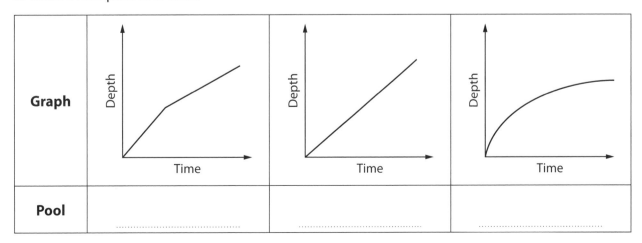

| | | | |
|---|---|---|---|
| **Graph** | | | |
| **Pool** | .................... | .................... | .................... |

**[ ___ / 2 marks]**

# Sequences

**1.** Complete the table for each sequence. The first one has been done for you.

|  | Sequence | Term-to-term rule | Next term | Seventh term | Type of sequence |
|---|---|---|---|---|---|
| **e.g.** | 2, 6, 10, 14 | Add 4 | 18 | 26 | Arithmetic |
| **a)** | 25, 31, 37, 43 |  |  |  |  |
| **b)** | 1, 2, 4, 8 |  |  |  |  |
| **c)** | 20, 10, 5, 2.5 |  |  |  |  |
| **d)** | 20, 17, 14, 11 |  |  |  |  |

**[I got ___ / 16 marks]**

**2.** Here are the first four terms of a number sequence.

$$12 \qquad 17 \qquad 22 \qquad 27$$

**a)** Nick says that the number 3075 will not be in this sequence. Is Nick correct? Give a reason for your answer.

.................................................................................................................... **[ ___ / 1 mark]**

**b)** Work out the 10th term in the sequence.

.................................................................................................................... **[ ___ / 2 marks]**

**3.** The first three patterns in a sequence of dots are pictured.

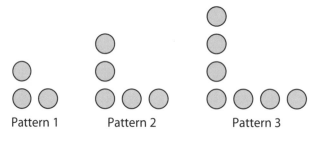

Pattern 1      Pattern 2      Pattern 3

**a)** How many dots will there be in Pattern 5?

.................................................................................................................... **[ ___ / 1 mark]**

**b)** What is the term-to-term rule for the number of dots in this sequence?

.................................................................................................................... **[ ___ / 1 mark]**

**c)** Is it possible for one of the patterns in the sequence to contain 20 dots? Give a reason for your answer.

> **Hint**
> What do you notice about all the numbers in the sequence?

.................................................................................................................... **[ ___ / 1 mark]**

**4.** The first four terms of an arithmetic sequence are $a$, 9, 15, $b$. Write the value of $a$ and the value of $b$.

.................................................................................................................... **[ ___ / 2 marks]**

# Using the *n*th term

Grade 3

1. Complete the table for each sequence. The first one has been done for you.

| | Position-to-term rule (*n*th term) | First four terms | Term-to-term rule | Seventh term | Hundredth term |
|---|---|---|---|---|---|
| e.g. | $2n + 6$ | 8, 10, 12, 14 | Add 2 | 20 | 206 |
| a) | $3n - 1$ | | | | |
| b) | $5n + 2$ | | | | |
| c) | $6 - n$ | | | | |
| d) | $10 - 3n$ | | | | |

**[I got ___ / 16 marks]**

Grade 3

2. Work out the first four terms of the sequences with these *n*th term rules.

a) $n^2 + 5$

......................................................................... **[ ___ / 2 marks]**

b) $n^2 - 2n$

......................................................................... **[ ___ / 2 marks]**

c) $10 - n^2$

......................................................................... **[ ___ / 2 marks]**

Grade 4

3. The *n*th term of a sequence is $8n + 3$

a) Which term in the sequence is 51?

......................................................................... **[ ___ / 2 marks]**

b) Show that 64 is not a number in the sequence.




......................................................................... **[ ___ / 2 marks]**

c) Work out the first number in the sequence to exceed 100

> **Hint**
> *Write and solve an inequality.*


......................................................................... **[ ___ / 3 marks]**

Grade 4

4. The *n*th term of a sequence is $n^2 - 30$

a) Work out the 4th number in the sequence.

......................................................................... **[ ___ / 2 marks]**

b) Is the number 114 in this sequence? Give a reason for your answer.

......................................................................... **[ ___ / 2 marks]**

# Working out the nth term

1. Complete the table for each sequence. The first one has been done for you.

|  | Sequence | Term-to-term rule | Position-to-term rule (nth term) | Tenth term |
|---|---|---|---|---|
| e.g. | 2, 6, 10, 14 | Add 4 | $4n - 2$ | $(4 \times 10) - 2 = 38$ |
| a) | 17, 23, 29, 35 |  |  |  |
| b) | −1, 2, 5, 8 |  |  |  |
| c) | 4, 1, −2, −5 |  |  |  |
| d) | 20, 15, 10, 5 |  |  |  |
| e) | 3, 3.5, 4, 4.5 |  |  |  |

**[I got ___ / 15 marks]**

2. The first three patterns in a sequence of dots are pictured.

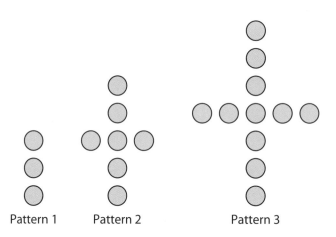

Pattern 1    Pattern 2    Pattern 3

**a)** Work out an expression, in terms of $n$, for the number of dots in the $n$th term of the sequence.

.................................................................................. **[ ___ / 2 marks]**

**b)** How many dots would there be in Pattern 40?

.................................................................................. **[ ___ / 2 marks]**

3. Here is a number sequence.

$$9, 14, 19, 24, \ldots$$

Emilia says the $n$th term of the sequence is $n + 5$. Isabella says the $n$th term of the sequence is $5n + 4$. Who is correct? Give a reason for your answer.

.................................................................................................................. **[ ___ / 1 mark]**

4. An arithmetic sequence has first term 5 and third term 11
What is the $n$th term of the sequence?

> **Hint**
> Work out some terms in the sequence first.

.................................................. **[ ___ / 2 marks]**

# Special sequences

**Grade 3**

**1.** Write the names of each of these special sequences.

**a)** 1, 4, 9, 16, 25, 36, …

..................................................... **[I got ___ / 1 mark]**

**b)** 1, 1, 2, 3, 5, 8, …

..................................................... **[ ___ / 1 mark]**

**c)** 1, 8, 27, 64, 125, 216, …

..................................................... **[ ___ / 1 mark]**

**Grade 3**

**2.** The first three patterns in a sequence of dots are pictured.

Pattern 1          Pattern 2          Pattern 3

**a)** Write the number of circles in the 4th pattern.

..................................................... **[ ___ / 1 mark]**

**b)** Write a rule for the th term of the sequence.

..................................................... **[ ___ / 1 mark]**

**Grade 4**

**3. a)** A Fibonacci-type sequence begins with these terms.

2    4    6    10    16

What is the 8th term in the sequence?

> **Hint**
> A Fibonacci-type sequence adds together
> two previous terms to get the next term.

..................................................... **[ ___ / 2 marks]**

**b)** Another Fibonacci-type sequence begins with these terms.

2    3

**i)** Write, in terms of , the next two terms in the sequence.

..................................................... **[ ___ / 2 marks]**

**ii)** If the 5th term of the sequence is 32, work out the value of the first term in the sequence.

..................................................... **[ ___ / 2 marks]**

**49**

# Proportion

**1.** Work out 32 grams as a proportion of 40 grams.

Give your answer as a percentage.

..................................................... **[I got __ / 2 marks]**

**2.** A ribbon of length 135 cm is cut to be 105 cm long.

Work out the new length as a proportion of the old length.

Give your answer as a fraction in its simplest form.

..................................................... **[ __ / 2 marks]**

**3.** The population of a small village has increased from 5000 to 7000

What is the new population as a percentage of its previous value? Circle your answer.

140%          60%          100.4%          99.6%          **[ __ / 1 mark]**

**4.** Jazmine scores 21 out of 30 in an algebra test and 18 out of 25 in a trigonometry test.

She argues that her algebra score is better.

Is she right? Give a reason for your answer.

.....................................................................................................

..................................................... **[ __ / 3 marks]**

**5.** In a cinema, the main feature plays for $1\frac{3}{4}$ hours. Before the film starts, there

are 0.25 hours of film previews, as well as 10 minutes of advertisements.

Work out the proportion of the total time for which the main feature plays.

Give your answer as a fraction in its simplest form.

> **Hint**
> Convert all times into the same units.

..................................................... **[ __ / 3 marks]**

**6.** In a theatre, $\frac{2}{3}$ of the audience are adults. $\frac{1}{4}$ of the children in the audience wear glasses.

What proportion of the theatre audience are children who don't wear

glasses?

> **Hint**
> Draw a bar model to help you. Remind yourself of how to multiply fractions.

..................................................... **[ __ / 3 marks]**

# Ratio

**1.** Work out the ratio 36:84 in its simplest form. Circle your answer.

9:21       21:9       7:3       3:7       **[I got ___ / 1 mark]**

**2.** The ratio of red balls to yellow balls on a pool table is 4:3

Work out the fraction of the balls that are red.

........................................................................... **[ ___ / 1 mark]**

**3.** $\frac{2}{3}$ of Lexi's class walk to school.

Write the ratio of students who **don't** walk to school to students who walk to school in Lexi's class.

........................................................................... **[ ___ / 1 mark]**

**4.** A recipe states that 75 grams of sultanas are needed to make 10 fruit scones.

Noah wants to make 12 fruit scones.

Work out how many grams of sultanas Noah needs.

> **Hint**
> Consider just one scone (or two scones) first.

........................................................... grams     **[ ___ / 2 marks]**

**5.** The ratio of the cost of weather-resistant treated rope to the cost of untreated rope is 4:3

Complete the table showing the costs of different lengths of rope, assuming the price per metre is fixed.

|            | 2 metres | 4 metres | 11 metres |
|------------|----------|----------|-----------|
| **Treated**   |          | £6.00    |           |
| **Untreated** |          |          |           |

**[ ___ / 3 marks]**

**6.** The lengths of the sides of a right-angled triangle are in the ratio 5:12:13

The shortest side has a length of 2 cm. What is the perimeter of the triangle?

> **Hint**
> This question combines ratio and geometry. Start by dividing each part of the ratio by 5

........................................................... cm     **[ ___ / 3 marks]**

# Using ratio

**Grade 4**

1. A 270 ml glass of orange squash contains water and orange cordial in the ratio of 8 : 1

   Work out how much water is in the glass. Circle your answer.

   240 ml          80 ml          30 ml          10 ml          **[I got ___ / 1 mark]**

**Grade 4**

2. In a card game, the ratio of losing cards to winning cards is 11 : 3

   If there are 70 cards in the batch, how many of the cards are winning cards?

   ................................................................................ **[ ___ / 2 marks]**

**Grade 4**

3. Martha mixes white paint with red paint in the ratio 2 : 3

   If she uses 9 litres of red paint, how much white paint does she use?

   ................................................................ litres     **[ ___ / 2 marks]**

**Grade 4**

4. In a Geography exam, there is a shorter paper and a longer paper.

   The marks are in the ratio 3 : 4. The total for both papers is 98

   How many marks are there on the shorter paper?

   ................................................................................ **[ ___ / 2 marks]**

**Grade 4**

5. The angles in a triangle are in the ratio 3 : 2 : 3

   a) Write down the name of this type of triangle.

   ................................................................................ **[ ___ / 1 mark]**

   b) Work out the size of the smallest angle in the triangle.

   > **Hint**
   > What is the sum of the
   > angles in a triangle?

   ....................................................° **[ ___ / 3 marks]**

**Grade 5**

6. The ratio of pencils to erasers in a school stockroom is 7 : 2

   There are 90 more pencils than erasers.

   How many pencils are there?

   ................................................................................ **[ ___ / 2 marks]**

# Percentage change

**1.** Increase £50 000 by 3%.

£........................................................ [I got ___ / 2 marks]

**2.** A puddle of water has a volume of 4 litres.

During a sunny spell, the puddle decreases to a volume of 2.5 litres.

By what percentage has the volume of the puddle decreased?

........................................................ [ ___ / 2 marks]

**3.** Harvey draws a line of length 4 cm.

He then extends the length of the line to 5 cm.

Work out the percentage increase in the length of his line. Circle your answer.

> **Hint**
> Area of square =
> length × length

1%          11%          20%          25%          [ ___ / 1 mark]

**4.** The table shows Kenny's weekly test scores in English and Maths.

|         | Week 1 | Week 2 | Week 3 | Week 4 |
|---------|--------|--------|--------|--------|
| **Maths**   | 50     | 62     | 78     | 90     |
| **English** | 58     | 58     | 57     |        |

The total of Kenny's English scores is 15% lower than the total of his Maths scores.

Work out the missing English score in the table.

........................................................ [ ___ / 4 marks]

**5.** At the age of 10, Talia's dog weighed 20 kg.

At the age of 12, the mass of her dog had increased by the same percentage as the age.

What is the mass of Talia's dog at the age of 12?

> **Hint**
> % increase = $\frac{actual\ increase}{original\ value}$ × 100%

........................................................ kg    [ ___ / 4 marks]

# Multipliers

**Grade 4**

**1.** A number is multiplied by 1.4

By what percentage does the number increase? Circle your answer.

| 0.4% | 4% | 40% | 400% | **[I got ___ / 1 mark]** |

**Grade 5**

**2. a)** Use a multiplier to increase 50 by 10%.

..................................................... **[ ___ / 2 marks]**

**b)** Use a multiplier to decrease 40 by 55%.

..................................................... **[ ___ / 2 marks]**

**Grade 5**

**3.** In a cricket match, the bowler releases the ball at a speed of 90 miles per hour.

The next ball bowled is 7% slower.

Use a multiplier to determine the speed of the slower ball.

............................................. mph    **[ ___ / 2 marks]**

**Grade 5**

**4.** £2450 is invested in a bank with a rate of 6% interest per year.

Work out the total amount that is in the bank account after two years if the account earns

**a)** simple interest

£................................................ **[ ___ / 3 marks]**

**b)** compound interest.

> **Hint**
> Compound interest is when the interest also earns interest.

£................................................ **[ ___ / 3 marks]**

**Grade 5**

**5.** A population of mayflies is decreasing at a rate of 4% per year.

Initially, the population is 3 000 000

Calculate the population after two years.

..................................................... **[ ___ / 3 marks]**

# Original value problems

**Grade 4**

**1.** A pair of jeans is £28 in a sale.

The sale price is a 30% reduction on the original price of the jeans.

Work out the original price of the jeans.

**Hint**
Work out what percentage of the original you have and then divide by this percentage.

£................................................. **[I got ___ / 3 marks]**

**Grade 4**

**2.** A woman is training to run a marathon.

Today, she runs 23 miles, which is a 15% increase on the distance she ran yesterday.

Work out the distance she ran yesterday.

................................................. miles **[ ___ / 3 marks]**

**Grade 4**

**3.** After 20% VAT has been added, an e-reader costs £92.40

Work out the cost of the e-reader before the VAT is added.

£................................................. **[ ___ / 3 marks]**

**Grade 4**

**4.** An egg's mass decreases by 11% when you remove its shell.

After removing its shell, an egg weighs 44.5 grams.

Work out the mass of the egg before removing its shell.

................................................. grams **[ ___ / 3 marks]**

**Grade 4**

**5.** A savings account in a bank earns 3% compound interest per year.

An initial amount of money is deposited in the account and, after one year, there is a total of £278.10 in the bank account.

Calculate how much money was initially deposited in the account.

£................................................. **[ ___ / 3 marks]**

**Grade 5**

**6.** Gemma chooses a number and increases it by 20%.

She then writes down the answer and decreases it by 20%.

Ben says that Gemma's final answer is wrong because it isn't the same as the original number.

Is he right? Show your working.

**Hint**
In this question, you are not given the original value or the final value. Choose any number and try Gemma's calculations.

................................................. **[ ___ / 3 marks]**

# Compound measures

**Grade 3**

1. A train is travelling at 30 m/s. Work out how long it takes to travel 1020 m.

.................................................................. **[I got ___ / 2 marks]**

**Grade 3**

2. A factory worker is paid a total of £368 for 32 hours' work.

Work out the rate of pay in pounds per hour.

.................................................................. **[ ___ / 2 marks]**

**Grade 4**

3. Water is poured into an empty tank at a rate of 20 cm³/s.

After how long will the tank contain 2400 cm³ of water?

.................................................................. **[ ___ / 2 marks]**

**Grade 5**

4. The density of copper is 8.94 g/cm³.

Use your calculator to work out the mass of a piece of copper with a volume of 0.6 cm³. Circle your answer.

0.067 g          5.364 g          14.9 g          53.64 g          **[ ___ / 1 mark]**

**Grade 5**

5. A force of 36 N is applied to an area of 0.45 m².

Use your calculator to work out the pressure, stating the units in your answer.

.................................................................. **[ ___ / 2 marks]**

**Grade 5**

6. 5 m³ of wrought iron has a mass of 38 700 000 g.

Use your calculator to work out the density of the wrought iron in kg/m³.

**Hint**
*Look at the units first!*

.................................................................. **[ ___ / 3 marks]**

**Grade 5**

7. a) A garden snail travels 5.64 m at a speed of 0.047 km/h.

Work out how long it takes. Give your answer in minutes and seconds.

.................................................................. **[ ___ / 4 marks]**

b) A slug travels 0.78 metres per minute.

By converting this speed to km/h, determine whether the garden snail or the slug is faster. Give a reason for your answer.

.................................................................. 

.................................................................. **[ ___ / 3 marks]**

# Direct proportion

**1.** The conversion graph below can be used to convert between litres and pints.

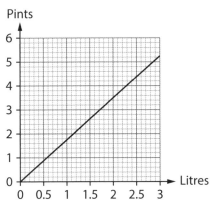

**a)** Use the graph to estimate what 2 litres is in pints.

.................................................. pints **[I got ___ / 2 marks]**

**b)** Use the graph to estimate what 4 pints is in litres.

.................................................. litres **[ ___ / 2 marks]**

**2.** Are the variables $x$ and $y$ in each of these equations in direct proportion?

Write **yes** if they are. Write **no** if they are not.

**a)** $y = \dfrac{1}{2}x$

.................................................. **[ ___ / 1 mark]**

**b)** $y = \dfrac{1}{x}$

.................................................. **[ ___ / 1 mark]**

**c)** $y + 5x = 0$

.................................................. **[ ___ / 1 mark]**

**d)** $y = x^2 - 1$

.................................................. **[ ___ / 1 mark]**

**3.** The variables $x$ and $y$ are in direct proportion. Below is a table of values.

| $x$ | 0 | 1 | 2 | 3 | 4 |
|-----|---|---|---|---|---|
| $y$ |   |   | 3 | 4.5 | 6 |

**a)** Complete the table. **[ ___ / 2 marks]**

**b)** Write the equation of the line. .................................................. **[ ___ / 1 mark]**

**4.** $y$ is directly proportional to $x$. When $x$ is 3, $y$ is 9

**a)** Write the value of $y$ when $x$ is 4

.................................................. **[ ___ / 2 marks]**

**b)** Write the value of $x$ when $y$ is 21

.................................................. **[ ___ / 2 marks]**

**c)** Write an equation for $y$ in terms of $x$

.................................................. **[ ___ / 1 mark]**

**5.** 'Dogs Love Bach' sells dog food in 3 kg bags. They are offering three bags for £12.99
'Woof & Ready' sells the same dog food in 2 kg bags. They are offering four bags for £11.00
Which dog food seller is offering better value? Show your working.

> **Hint**
> Divide to get the value of
> 1 unit e.g. the cost of 1 kg.

.................................................. **[ ___ / 3 marks]**

# Inverse proportion

**1.** A team of 12 builders can complete the building of a house in six days.

**a)** How many days would it take 18 builders?

............................................... days    **[I got ___ / 2 marks]**

**b)** Write how many builders would be needed to complete the house in three days.

............................................... **[ ___ / 2 marks]**

**2.** Three hosepipes are used to fill a swimming pool with water in 30 hours.

**a)** Write how long it would take with four hosepipes.

............................................... hours    **[ ___ / 2 marks]**

**b)** Write how many hosepipes would be needed to fill the pool in 10 hours.

............................................... **[ ___ / 2 marks]**

**3.** Which one of these graphs shows an inversely proportional relationship? Circle your answer.

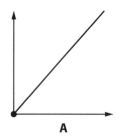 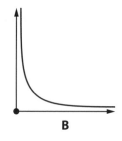 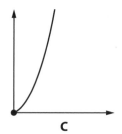 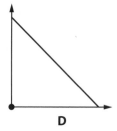

      **A**            **B**            **C**            **D**

**[ ___ / 1 mark]**

**4. a)** $y$ is inversely proportional to $x$. Which of these could be equations for $y$?

$$y = \frac{6}{x} \qquad y = x^2 \qquad y = \sqrt{x}$$

............................................... **[ ___ / 1 mark]**

**b)** Using your equation from part **a**, write the value of $y$ when $x = 4$

............................................... **[ ___ / 1 mark]**

**c)** Using your equation from part **a**, write the value of $x$ when $y = 1$

............................................... **[ ___ / 1 mark]**

# Time and timetables

Grade 1
1. a) Write the time 06:35 as a 12-hour clock time.

......................................................... **[I got ___ / 1 mark]**

b) Write the time 5:20 pm as a 24-hour clock time.

......................................................... **[ ___ / 1 mark]**

Grade 1
2. A theatre show starts at 7:31 pm.

The show is scheduled to last for 2 hours and 15 minutes. The current time is 8:24 pm.

Work out how much of the show is left. Give your answer in hours and minutes.

......................................................... **[ ___ / 2 marks]**

Grade 2
3. Siobhan uses her calculator to solve a question about time.

Her calculator shows an answer of 3.4 hours.

> **Hint**
> To convert a decimal part of an hour to minutes, multiply by 60

a) What is Siobhan's answer in hours and minutes?
Circle your answer.

34 minutes      3 hours 4 minutes      3 hours 24 minutes      3 hours 40 minutes      **[ ___ / 1 mark]**

On another question, Siobhan successfully converts a time from decimal form to 1 hour 48 minutes.

b) What was the time in decimal form?

......................................................... hours      **[ ___ / 2 marks]**

Grade 3
4. This timetable shows the bus times for three small villages, Aust, Brant and Chenk.

| Aust  | 11:20 | 12:20 | 13:20 | –     | 15:20 | 16:20 |
|-------|-------|-------|-------|-------|-------|-------|
| Brant | 11:35 | 12:35 | 13:35 | –     | 15:35 | 17:35 |
| Chenk | 11:40 | 12:40 | 13:40 | –     | 15:40 | 17:40 |
|       |       |       |       |       |       |       |
| Chenk | 11:45 | 12:45 | –     | 14:40 | 15:45 | 17:45 |
| Brant | –     | –     | –     | 14:45 | 15:50 | 17:50 |
| Aust  | 12:10 | 13:10 | –     | 15:00 | 16:05 | 18:05 |

a) Write the time that the 15:20 bus from Aust arrives at Chenk.

......................................................... **[ ___ / 1 mark]**

b) Wilf gets the 12:20 from Aust and gets off the bus at Brant. It takes him 10 minutes to walk to his friend's house, where he then stays for 2 hours and 45 minutes. Another 10 minute walk to the bus stop follows, where he then gets the next available bus back to Aust. At what time does Wilf arrive back in Aust? Show your working in full.

......................................................... **[ ___ / 3 marks]**

# Measures

**1. a)** Draw a straight line of length 5.4 cm.

[I got ___ / 1 mark]

**b)** Measure the total perimeter of the triangle in mm.

.................................................................... mm    [ ___ / 2 marks]

**2.** Write down suitable metric units for measuring each of these items.

**a)** The diameter of a 10p coin

.................................................................... [ ___ / 1 mark]

**b)** The mass of a chocolate bar

.................................................................... [ ___ / 1 mark]

**c)** The volume of wine in a wine glass

.................................................................... [ ___ / 1 mark]

**3.** Convert 17 centimetres into millimetres. Circle your answer.

0.017 mm          1.7 mm          170 mm          17000 mm          [ ___ / 1 mark]

**4. a)** Convert 2500 milligrams into grams.

.................................................... grams    [ ___ / 1 mark]

**b)** Convert 0.35 litres into millilitres.

.................................................... ml    [ ___ / 1 mark]

**5.** A bag contains 36 ounces (oz) of sugar.

Another bag contains 2 pounds (lbs) of flour.

In this question, use 1 oz = 28 g and 1 lb = 0.45 kg.

Work out the total weight of the bags in kg.

> **Hint**
> You will need to convert g into kg in this question.

.................................................... kg    [ ___ / 3 marks]

**6.** Olivia is 68 inches tall.

If 1 foot = 12 inches, how tall is Olivia in feet and inches?

.................................................... [ ___ / 2 marks]

# Scale drawing

**1.** The giraffe is 6 metres tall.

**a)** Estimate the height of the camel in metres.

6 m

........................................................................ m    **[I got ___ / 1 mark]**

**b)** A scale drawing of the giraffe is made using 3 cm to represent 1 m. What is the height of the giraffe in the scale drawing in centimetres?

........................................................................ cm    **[ ___ / 1 mark]**

**2.** The Seattle Space Needle is 184 metres tall.

How tall is a 1:2000 scale model in centimetres? Circle your answer.

     0.92 cm         9.2 cm         92 cm         920 cm      **[ ___ / 1 mark]**

**3. a)** A map uses a scale of 2 cm to represent 5 kilometres.

Write this ratio in the form $1:n$

> **Hint**
> Convert km to cm.

........................................................................    **[ ___ / 2 marks]**

**b)** A different map uses a scale of 1:400 000

Work out how many kilometres are represented by 5 cm on the map.

........................................................................ km    **[ ___ / 2 marks]**

**4.** A rectangular netball court is 30.5 m long and 15.25 m wide.

Using 1 cm to represent 5 m, draw an accurate scale drawing of the netball court in the space below.

**[ ___ / 3 marks]**

# Angles

**1. a)** Write the name of the type of each angle shown.

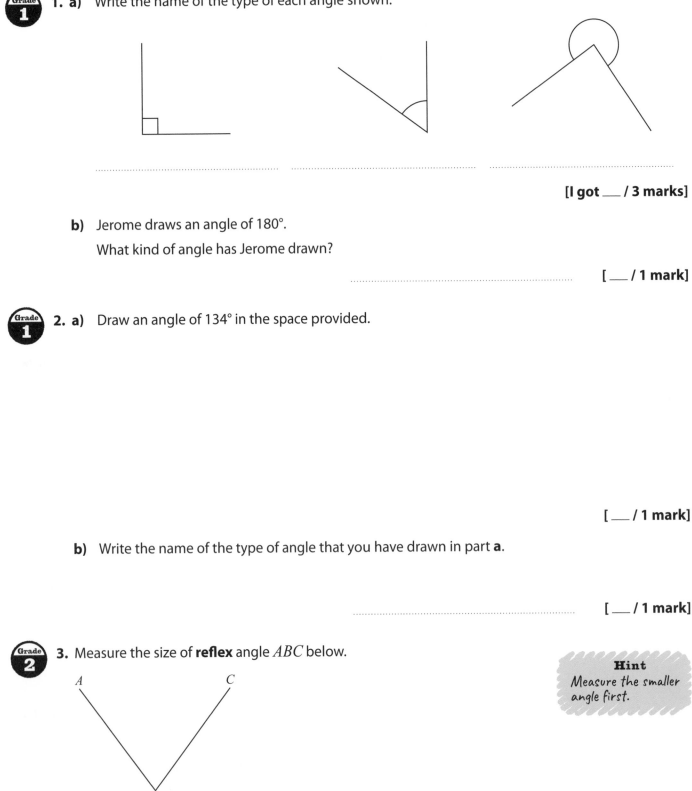

.......................................... .......................................... ..........................................

**[I got ___ / 3 marks]**

**b)** Jerome draws an angle of 180°.

What kind of angle has Jerome drawn?

.......................................... **[ ___ / 1 mark]**

**2. a)** Draw an angle of 134° in the space provided.

**[ ___ / 1 mark]**

**b)** Write the name of the type of angle that you have drawn in part **a**.

.......................................... **[ ___ / 1 mark]**

**3.** Measure the size of **reflex** angle *ABC* below.

**Hint**
Measure the smaller angle first.

.......................................... ° **[ ___ / 2 marks]**

**4.** Khabib says that if you add together two acute angles, you always get an obtuse angle.

Give an example to show that Khabib is wrong.

.......................................... **[ ___ / 1 mark]**

# Angle rules

**1.** Work out the size of angle $x$ in the diagram.

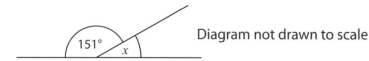

Diagram not drawn to scale

........................................° **[I got ___ / 2 marks]**

**2.** The hour-hand of a clock is pointing directly at the number 1

How many degrees does it have to turn before it points directly at number 5? Circle your answer.

60°          90°          120°          1500°          **[ ___ / 1 mark]**

**3.**

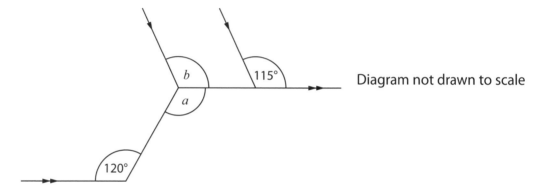

Diagram not drawn to scale

From the diagram, write the sizes of angles $a$ and $b$, giving a reason for each answer.

**a)**  $a =$ ........................° Reason: ....................................... **[ ___ / 2 marks]**

**b)**  $b =$ ........................° Reason: ....................................... **[ ___ / 2 marks]**

**4.** By forming and solving a suitable equation, work out the size of $y$ in the diagram.

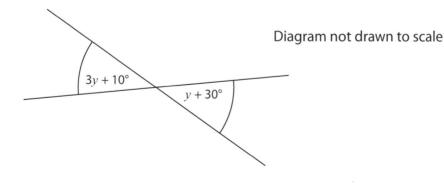

Diagram not drawn to scale

**Hint**
Here, angle rules and algebra
are combined. Remind yourself
how to solve equations.

........................................° **[ ___ / 3 marks]**

# Bearings

**1. a)** Write the three-figure bearing for east.

.................................................° **[I got ___ / 1 mark]**

**b)** Give the angle between north-west and south-east.

.................................................° **[ ___ / 1 mark]**

**2.** The bearing of $P$ from $Q$ is 130°. What is the bearing of $Q$ from $P$?

> **Hint**
> Draw a diagram to help you.

.................................................° **[ ___ / 2 marks]**

**3. a)** Measure the bearing of $B$ from $A$ in the diagram.

North

B

A

.................................................° **[ ___ / 1 mark]**

**b)** On the diagram, draw a line on a bearing of 110° from $B$.   **[ ___ / 1 mark]**

**4.** Work out the bearing of $Q$ from $P$ in the diagram.

North

Diagram not drawn to scale

30°   P

Q

> **Hint**
> Remember that you want the clockwise angle!

.................................................° **[ ___ / 2 marks]**

**5.** A speedboat ($S$) is positioned due east of a dinghy ($D$). The bearing of a hovercraft ($H$) from the Dinghy ($D$) is 080°. The bearing of the same hovercraft from the speedboat is 280°. On the diagram, draw the position of the hovercraft. Label it $H$.

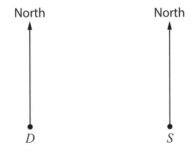

North

North

D

S

**[ ___ / 3 marks]**

# Triangles & quadrilaterals

 **1.** Circle the name of the type of quadrilateral shown.

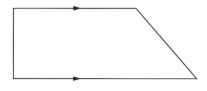

        Rhombus        Trapezium        Parallelogram        Kite        **[I got ___ / 1 mark]**

 **2.** Work out the size of angle $y$ in the triangle shown.

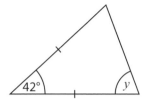

Diagram not drawn to scale          .................................................°    **[ ___ / 2 marks]**

 **3.** The quadrilateral $ABCD$ is a rhombus.

Work out the size of angle $x$. Show your working, giving your reasons for each step.

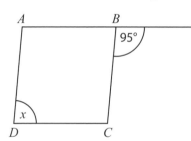         Diagram not drawn to scale

         .................................................°    **[ ___ / 3 marks]**

 **4.** The four angles of a quadrilateral are $x$, $2x$, $3x$ and $2x + 20°$.

Work out the size of the smallest angle.

> **Hint**
> Form an equation in x and solve.

         .................................................°    **[ ___ / 3 marks]**

 **5.** In the diagram, angle $BFA$ is 44°. Work out the size of angle $FDE$.

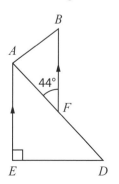

Diagram not drawn to scale          .................................................°    **[ ___ / 3 marks]**

# Polygons

**1. a)** Circle the name of a 5-sided polygon.

Hexagon          Heptagon          Pentagon          Decagon          **[I got ___ / 1 mark]**

**b)** What makes a polygon 'regular'?

......................................................................................................................................................................................... **[ ___ / 1 mark]**

**2.** Part of a regular polygon is shown, along with its exterior angle.

Write the name of the shape. Give a reason for your answer.

Diagram not drawn to scale

60°

......................................................................................................................................................................................... **[ ___ / 2 marks]**

**3.** An irregular hexagon contains interior angles with sizes 41°, 59°, 83°, 90° and 147°.

Calculate the size of its remaining interior angle.

.......................................................................................° **[ ___ / 3 marks]**

**4.** The diagram shows a square, two equilateral triangles and two regular octagons.

Work out the size of angle $x$.

$x$

> **Hint**
> Consider the rule for
> the sum of angles
> around a point.

Diagram not drawn to scale          ...........................................................° **[ ___ / 4 marks]**

**5.** Jemima says she has drawn a regular polygon with an interior angle of 80°.

Sophia says that it is impossible.

Who is correct? Give a reason for your answer.

> **Hint**
> Work out the size of
> an exterior angle.

.........................................................................................................................................................................................

......................................................................................................................................................................................... **[ ___ / 3 marks]**

# Reflection

**1. a)** Reflect shape $A$ in the mirror line shown. Label the image $A'$.

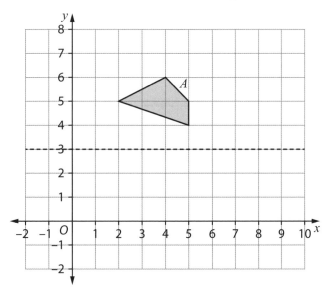

**Hint**
Reflect one vertex at a time.

**[I got ___ / 2 marks]**

**b)** Write the equation of the mirror line.

....................................................................... **[ ___ / 1 mark]**

**2.** Describe fully the single transformation that maps shape $A$ to shape $B$.

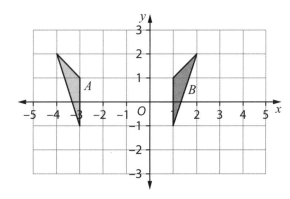

....................................................................... **[ ___ / 2 marks]**

**3. a)** Reflect shape $P$ in the mirror line shown. Label the image $Q$.

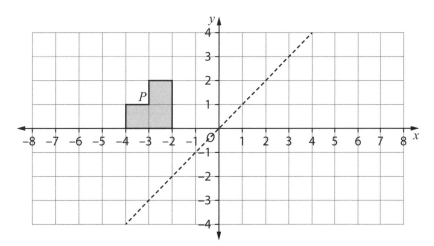

**[ ___ / 2 marks]**

**b)** Write the equation of the mirror line.

....................................................................... **[ ___ / 1 mark]**

# Rotation

**1.** A point $P$ with coordinates (1, 2) is rotated 180° about the origin to a point $P'$.

What are the coordinates of the point $P'$? Circle your answer.

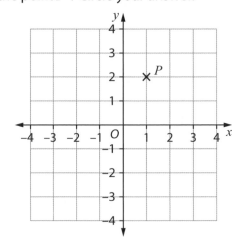

(2, 1)        (−1, 2)        (−1, −2)        (1, −2)        **[I got ___ / 1 mark]**

**2. a)** On the grid shown, rotate shape $A$ 90° anticlockwise about the point (2, 3). Label the image $B$.

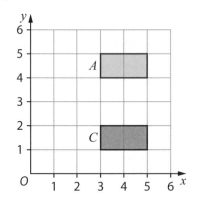

**[ ___ / 2 marks]**

**b)** Describe the rotation that maps shape $A$ to shape $C$.

**Hint**
Your description will be similar to that given in part a.

**[ ___ / 2 marks]**

**3. a)** On the grid shown, rotate triangle $P$ 180° about the origin.

Label the image $Q$.        **[ ___ / 2 marks]**

**b)** Triangle $P$ is rotated 90° anticlockwise about the point (0, 2) onto one of the other triangles in the grid. Which triangle is it?

**[ ___ / 1 mark]**

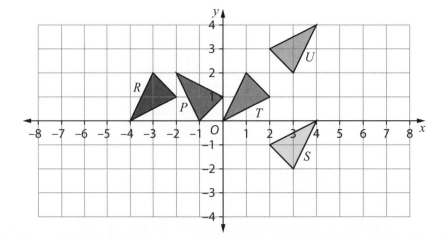

# Translation

**1.** Circle the column vector that represents the translation 'three squares to the left and four squares up'.

$$\begin{pmatrix} -3 \\ -4 \end{pmatrix} \qquad \begin{pmatrix} -3 \\ 4 \end{pmatrix} \qquad \begin{pmatrix} 3 \\ -4 \end{pmatrix} \qquad \begin{pmatrix} 3 \\ 4 \end{pmatrix}$$

**[I got ___ / 1 mark]**

**2.** On the grid below, translate the T-shape using the column vector $\begin{pmatrix} 4 \\ 0 \end{pmatrix}$.

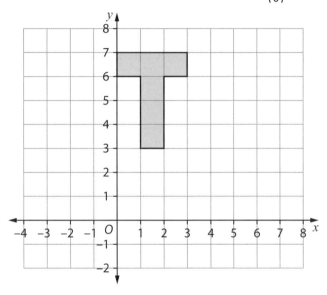

**[ ___ / 1 mark]**

**3. a)** Using a suitable column vector, describe the transformation that maps shape $A$ to shape $B$ in the grid below.

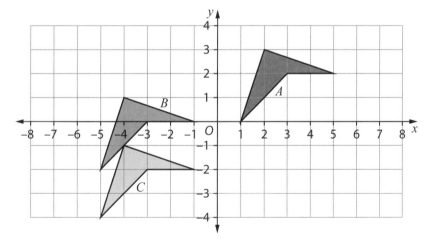

........................................................................ **[ ___ / 2 marks]**

**b) i)** The transformation that maps shape $C$ to shape $B$ is the same as the transformation that maps shape $B$ to shape $D$. Draw shape $D$ on the grid above. **[ ___ / 1 mark]**

**ii)** Describe fully the transformation that maps $D$ to $B$.

........................................................................ **[ ___ / 2 marks]**

**4.** Adam says he is going to translate a shape using the column vector $\begin{pmatrix} 0 \\ 0 \end{pmatrix}$.
Finbar says that the shape will be mapped to exactly the same position.
Is Finbar correct? Give a reason for your answer.

........................................................................ **[ ___ / 1 mark]**

# Enlargement

**1.** Which shape is an enlargement of shape $A$? Circle your answer.

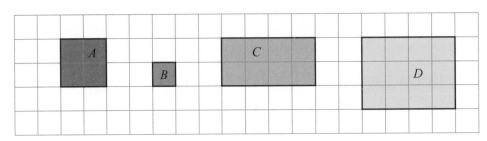

Shape $B$      Shape $C$      Shape $D$      None of them      **[I got ___ / 1 mark]**

**2.** Describe fully the transformation that maps rectangle $ABCD$ onto rectangle $A'B'C'D'$ in the grid shown.

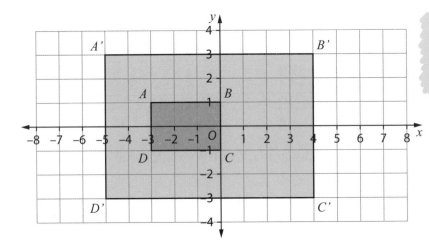

> **Hint**
> Draw lines through corresponding vertices and see where they meet.

......................................................................................................................................................... **[ ___ / 3 marks]**

**3.** Use this grid to answer the question.

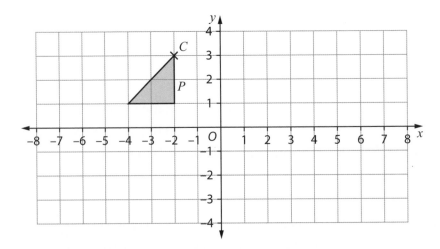

a) Enlarge triangle $P$ with scale factor 2, centre $C$. Label your image $Q$.      **[ ___ / 2 marks]**

b) Enlarge triangle $P$ with scale factor $\frac{1}{2}$, centre $(2, -1)$. Label your image $R$.      **[ ___ / 2 marks]**

# Congruent shapes

 **1.** Which shape is congruent to the first shape? Circle your answer.

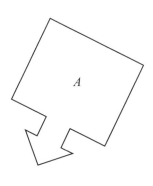   

**[I got ___ / 1 mark]**

 **2.** On the grid, shade three more squares so that shape $N$ is congruent to shape $M$.

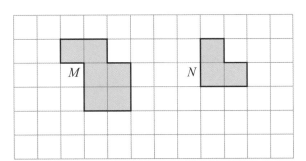

**[ ___ / 1 mark]**

 **3.** Give a reason (SSS, SAS, ASA or RHS) for why each pair of triangles is congruent.

**a)**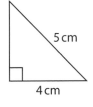

**b)**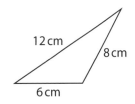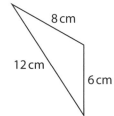

.................................................... ....................................................

**c)**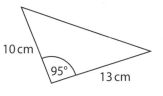

.................................................... **[ ___ / 3 marks]**

 **4.** The two triangles $ABC$ and $FED$ are congruent.

Diagrams not to scale

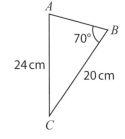 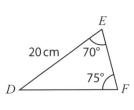

**a)** Write the length of $DF$. ............................................ **[ ___ / 1 mark]**

**b)** Write the size of angle $CAB$. ............................................ **[ ___ / 1 mark]**

# Similar shapes

**1.** Which rectangle is similar to the first rectangle? Circle your answer.

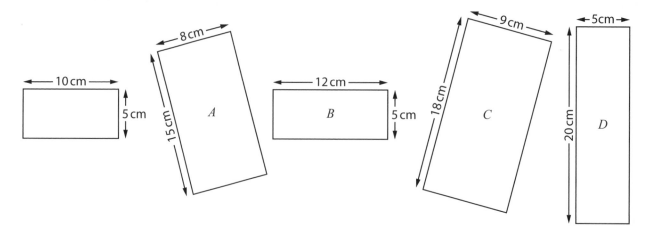

**[I got ___ / 1 mark]**

**2.** These two triangles are similar. Work out the length $y$.

Diagrams not to scale

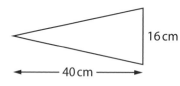

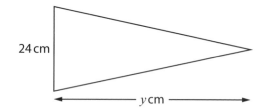

...................................................................... cm    **[ ___ / 2 marks]**

**3.** Show that these two triangles are similar.

> **Hint**
> Compare ratios of sides.

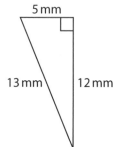

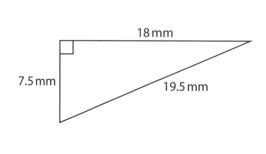

Diagrams not to scale

**[ ___ / 2 marks]**

**4.** In the diagram, $EB$ is parallel to $DC$. $ABE$ and $ACD$ are similar triangles. $AC = 11.5$ cm, $AB = 9.2$ cm and $AE = 8.4$ cm. Work out the length of $ED$.

Diagram not to scale

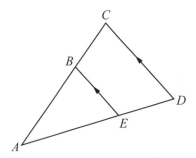

...................................................................... cm    **[ ___ / 2 marks]**

# Area and perimeter

**Grade 2**

**1.** Work out the area of these shapes.

**a)**

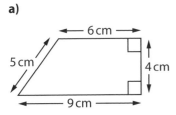

**b)**

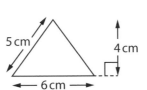

**c)**

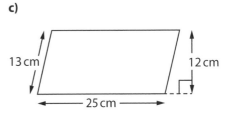

.................................... cm² .................................... cm² .................................... cm²

**[I got ___ / 6 marks]**

**Grade 3**

**2.** The length of the rectangle is twice the length of the square.

Work out the perimeter of the rectangle.

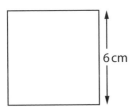

Diagrams not to scale

.................................... cm     **[ ___ / 2 marks]**

**Grade 4**

**3.** The perimeter of the £5 banknote is 380 mm. Work out the perimeter of the £10 banknote.

.................................... mm     **[ ___ / 3 marks]**

**Grade 4**

**4.** A parallelogram and a triangle have the same area. The parallelogram has a base of 12.8 cm and a height of $x$ cm. The triangle has a base of 12.8 cm and a height of 17.9 cm. Work out the length $x$.

> **Hint**
> You may want to sketch the shapes first.

.................................... cm     **[ ___ / 2 marks]**

**Grade 3**

1. For this compound shape, work out

   **a)** the perimeter

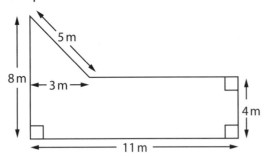

........................................................ m   **[I got ___ / 2 marks]**

   **b)** the area.

........................................................ m²   **[ ___ / 3 marks]**

**Grade 4**

2. Work out the area of this hexagon with equal sides.

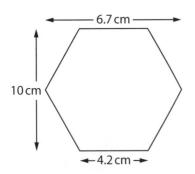

> **Hint**
> Divide the hexagon into
> two separate areas.

........................................................ cm²   **[ ___ / 2 marks]**

**Grade 4**

3. The flag of Denmark consists of a white cross on a red background.
   Work out the area of the white cross.

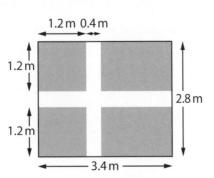

........................................................ m²   **[ ___ / 3 marks]**

# Circles

**Grade 3**

1. Giving your answers to 3 significant figures, work out

   **a)** the area of the circle

3 mm

**Hint**
Remind yourself of significant figures.

.................................................................. mm² **[I got ___ / 3 marks]**

   **b)** the circumference of the circle.

.................................................................. mm **[ ___ / 3 marks]**

**Grade 3**

2. **a)** Write the name of each of the circle parts indicated.

.................................................................. **[ ___ / 1 mark]**

.................................................................. **[ ___ / 1 mark]**

   **b)** On the diagram in part **a**, draw a chord. **[ ___ / 1 mark]**

**Grade 4**

3. Giving your answers in terms of π, work out

   **a)** the area of the circle

8 cm

.................................................................. cm² **[ ___ / 2 marks]**

   **b)** the circumference of the circle.

.................................................................. cm **[ ___ / 2 marks]**

**Grade 4**

4. A circle has an area of 25π cm². What is the circumference of the circle in terms of π?

**Hint**
Work out the radius of the circle.

.................................................................. cm **[ ___ / 2 marks]**

**Grade 5**

5. A circle of radius *r* is drawn.

   Hyacinth says that if the radius is halved, then the area will be halved as well.

   Is Hyacinth correct? You must show all of your working.

**Hint**
Choose your own value for *r*.

*r*

.................................................................. **[ ___ / 3 marks]**

# Semicircles

**1. a)** For this semicircle, work out

    **i)** the area, to 1 decimal place

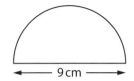

9 cm

.................................................... cm² **[I got ___ / 2 marks]**

    **ii)** the perimeter, to 1 decimal place.

.................................................... cm **[ ___ / 2 marks]**

**b)** Giving your answers to 3 significant figures and clearly stating your units, work out

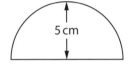

5 cm

    **i)** the area of the semicircle

.................................................... **[ ___ / 3 marks]**

    **ii)** the perimeter of the semicircle.

.................................................... **[ ___ / 3 marks]**

**2.** A sculpture is made using three semicircles and is arranged as shown in the diagram.

Work out the perimeter of the sculpture, giving your answer to 3 significant figures.

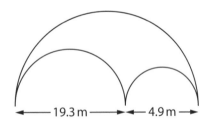

19.3 m ⟷ 4.9 m

> **Hint**
> You will need to know the diameters of all three semicircles.

.................................................... m **[ ___ / 3 marks]**

**3.** This compound shape is made using a semicircle on top of an isosceles trapezium.

Work out the area of the compound shape to 1 decimal place.

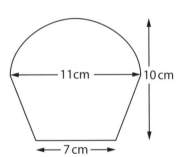

11 cm ⟷ 10 cm

7 cm

.................................................... cm² **[ ___ / 4 marks]**

# Arcs and sectors

**1.** Giving your answers to 1 decimal place and clearly stating your units, work out

    **a)** the area of the sector

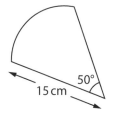

........................................................ [I got ___ / 3 marks]

    **b)** the arc length.

........................................................ [ ___ / 3 marks]

**2.** Work out, to 1 decimal place,

    **a)** the area of the sector

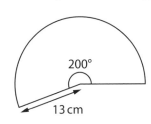

.................................................... cm² [ ___ / 2 marks]

    **b)** the arc length of the sector.

.................................................... cm [ ___ / 2 marks]

**3.** The circular cake shown has been cut into six identical slices. The radius of the cake is 18 cm.

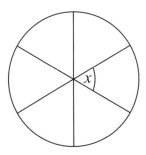

    **a)** Write the size of angle $x$. ........................................ ° [ ___ / 1 mark]

    **b)** Work out the area of a single slice of cake, giving your answer in terms of π.

.................................................... cm² [ ___ / 2 marks]

**4. a)** Work out the arc length of the sector. Give your answer in terms of π.

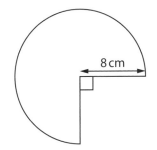

.................................................... cm [ ___ / 2 marks]

    **b)** Work out the area of the sector. Give your answer in terms of π.

.................................................... cm² [ ___ / 2 marks]

# 3D shapes

 **1.** Write the name of each of these 3D shapes.

**a)** 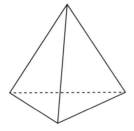      **b)** 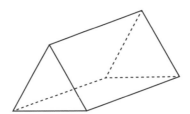      **c)**

..................................     ..................................     ..................................

**[I got ___ / 3 marks]**

 **2. a)** Circle the name of this 3D shape.

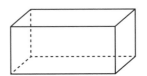

       Rectangle      Square      Cube      Cuboid      **[ ___ / 1 mark]**

**b)** Write how many of each of these the shape has.

    **i)** Faces                             .....................................................     **[ ___ / 1 mark]**

    **ii)** Vertices                     .....................................................     **[ ___ / 1 mark]**

    **iii)** Edges                           .....................................................     **[ ___ / 1 mark]**

 **3.** How many faces, edges and vertices does a pentagonal-based prism have?

..........................................................................................................................   **[ ___ / 3 marks]**

 **4.** Use the diagram of a square-based pyramid for this question.

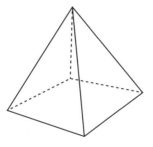

    **a)** Shade in exactly one face on the square-based pyramid.           **[ ___ / 1 mark]**

    **b)** Draw a circle around any one of its vertices.                **[ ___ / 1 mark]**

    **c)** Work out 'the number of faces + the number of vertices – the number of edges' for this shape.

..........................................................................................................................   **[ ___ / 2 marks]**

# Plans and elevations

Grade 3
**1.** The solid object is made from six identical cubes.

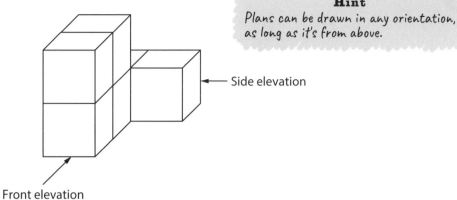

**Hint**
Plans can be drawn in any orientation, as long as it's from above.

Side elevation

Front elevation

On the grids below, draw the named elevations and the plan.

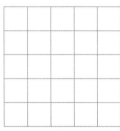
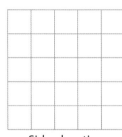
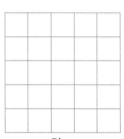

Front elevation     Side elevation     Plan

**[I got ___ / 3 marks]**

Grade 4
**2.** Here are the front and side elevations of a solid shape.

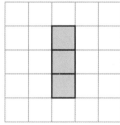
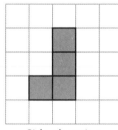
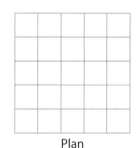

Front elevation     Side elevation     Plan

**a)** On the grid above, draw the plan of the solid shape.     **[ ___ / 1 mark]**

**b)** In the space below, draw a 3D sketch of the solid shape.

**[ ___ / 2 marks]**

# Nets and surface area

**1.** Which one of these is **not** a net of a cube? Circle your answer.

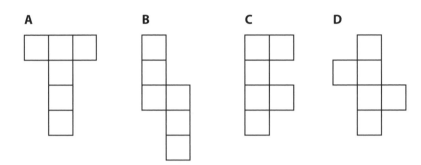

A  B  C  D

**2.** The net of a solid is shown.

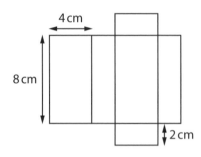

4 cm

8 cm

2 cm

a) Write the name of the solid. ................................................................ [ ___ / 1 mark]

b) Work out the surface area of the solid. Include units in your answer.

> **Hint**
> Use the net to help you.

................................................................ [ ___ / 3 marks]

**3.** A sketch of a triangular-based pyramid (also called a tetrahedron) is shown.

Each face of the pyramid is an equilateral triangle.

a) Draw a net of the triangular-based pyramid.

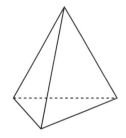

[ ___ / 2 marks]

b) Each equilateral triangle has a base length of 3 cm and a height of 2.6 cm. Work out the surface area of the triangular-based pyramid.

> **Hint**
> Start by finding the area of one triangle.

................................................................ cm² [ ___ / 2 marks]

# Prisms and cylinders

**1.** Work out the volume of the cuboid shown. Circle your answer.

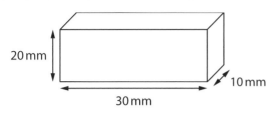

20 mm

30 mm

10 mm

    60 mm        60 mm³        6000 mm        6000 mm³      **[I got ___ / 1 mark]**

**2.** The hexagonal prism has a height of 8 m and a cross-sectional area of 25 m².

Work out the volume of the prism. State your units.

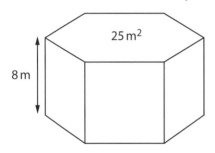

25 m²

8 m

                                                      **[ ___ / 2 marks]**

**3.** An unopened cylindrical baked beans can has a height of 11 cm and a radius of 4 cm. Work out

**a)** the volume of the baked beans can in terms of $\pi$

                                         cm³    **[ ___ / 2 marks]**

**b)** the surface area of the baked beans can to 3 significant figures.

> **Hint**
> A closed cylinder has three surfaces.

                                         cm²    **[ ___ / 4 marks]**

**4.** The triangular prisms shown both have the same volume. Work out the height $h$. State your units.

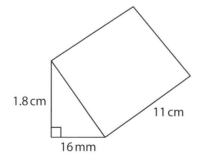
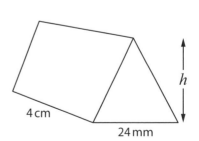

1.8 cm        11 cm

16 mm

4 cm        24 mm     $h$

                                                      **[ ___ / 4 marks]**

# Spheres

$$\text{Volume of a sphere} = \frac{4}{3}\pi r^3 \quad \text{Surface area of a sphere} = 4\pi r^2$$

**1.** A sphere has a surface area of 40 cm². Convert the surface area to mm². Circle your answer.

      4 mm²       400 mm²       4000 mm²       40000 mm²       **[I got ___ / 1 mark]**

**2.** A sphere has a volume of 120 cm³. Convert the volume to m³.

....................................................................... m³    **[ ___ / 2 marks]**

**3.** A sphere has a radius of 18.2 cm.

Calculate, to 1 decimal place,

    **a)** the volume of the sphere

....................................................................... cm³    **[ ___ / 2 marks]**

    **b)** the surface area of the sphere.

....................................................................... cm²    **[ ___ / 2 marks]**

**4.** A sphere has a radius of 5 cm. Work out

    **a)** the volume of the sphere in terms of π

....................................................................... cm³    **[ ___ / 2 marks]**

    **b)** the surface area of the sphere in terms of π. State your units.

.......................................................................     **[ ___ / 3 marks]**

**5.** A sphere has a surface area of 400π cm². Work out the radius of the sphere.

> **Hint**
> Form and solve an equation for r.

....................................................................... cm    **[ ___ / 2 marks]**

# Pyramids and cones

$$\text{Volume of a cone} = \frac{1}{3}\pi r^2 h \quad \text{Curved surface area of a cone} = \pi r \ell$$

**1.** Use the diagram of the cone for this question.

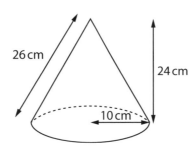

Work out, giving your answers in terms of $\pi$,

**a)** the volume of the cone

.................................................. cm$^3$ **[I got ___ / 2 marks]**

**b)** the surface area of the cone.

.................................................. cm$^2$ **[ ___ / 3 marks]**

**2.** The Great Pyramid of Giza has a square base of length 230 m and a height of 147 m.

Work out the volume of the pyramid to 2 significant figures.

> **Hint**
> Work out the area
> of the base first.

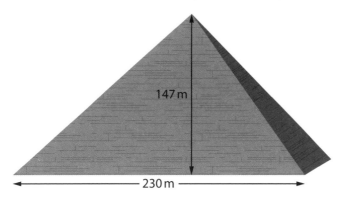

.................................................. m$^3$ **[ ___ / 3 marks]**

**3.** A cone, with a slant height of 7 cm, has a curved surface area of 21$\pi$ cm$^2$.

Work out the area of the circular base of the cone to 1 decimal place.

.................................................. cm$^2$ **[ ___ / 3 marks]**

# Constructing triangles

**1. a)** Only one of these triangles can be constructed. Circle its letter.

     **A** A triangle with sides 7 cm, 8 cm and 16 cm      **B** A triangle with sides 3 cm, 4 cm and 6 cm

     **C** A triangle with sides 9 cm, 12 cm and 22 cm      **D** A triangle with sides 15 cm, 30 cm and 60 cm

**[I got ___ / 1 mark]**

     **b)** Using a ruler and a pair of compasses, construct the triangle you have chosen in part **a**.

**[ ___ / 3 marks]**

**2.** Use a ruler and a protractor to draw this triangle accurately.

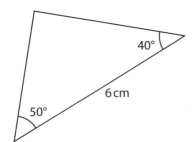

> **Hint**
> Start with the 6 cm line.

**[ ___ / 3 marks]**

**3.** Accurately draw triangle $ABC$ where $AB = 6.4$ cm, $AC = 4.8$ cm and angle $BAC = 120°$.

**[ ___ / 3 marks]**

**4.** Construct triangle $DEF$ where $DE = 66$ mm, $EF = \dfrac{2}{3} DE$ and $FD = \dfrac{3}{4} EF$.

**[ ___ / 3 marks]**

# Perpendiculars and bisectors

**1. a)** Using a ruler and a pair of compasses, construct the perpendicular bisector of the line segment *AB*. You must show your construction lines.

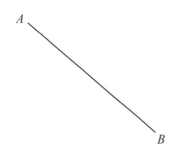

**[I got ___ / 2 marks]**

**b)** Using a ruler and a pair of compasses, construct the bisector of angle *CDE*. You must show your construction lines.

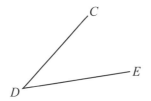

**[ ___ / 2 marks]**

**2.** Using a ruler and a pair of compasses, construct the perpendicular line to the line segment *FH* that passes through *G*. You must show your construction lines.

> **Hint**
> Start by drawing arcs either side of G.

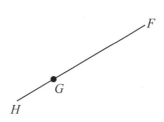

**[ ___ / 3 marks]**

**3.** Using a ruler and a pair of compasses, construct an angle of 45°.

You must show your construction lines.

**[ ___ / 3 marks]**

# Loci

**1.** Draw the locus of points that are exactly 2 cm from point $P$.

$P$

**[I got ___ / 2 marks]**

**2.** Shade the area that is further from $A$ than from $B$ but is less than 3 cm away from $B$.

Show all construction lines.

$A$ ———————————————— $B$

**[ ___ / 4 marks]**

**3.** A triangular plot of land is shown.

Milly farms the area of land that is closer to $CD$ than $CE$ and is also less than 500 m from $C$.

Shade the area of land that Milly farms. Show all construction lines.

> **Hint**
> You will need to draw a
> bisector and a circle.

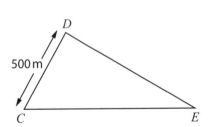

**[ ___ / 4 marks]**

**4.** Draw the locus of points that are exactly 2 cm away from the T-shape.

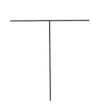

**[ ___ / 3 marks]**

# Pythagoras' theorem

 **1.** Only one of these triangles is right-angled. Circle its letter.

**A**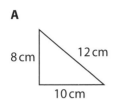
8 cm  12 cm  10 cm

**B**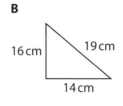
16 cm  19 cm  14 cm

**C**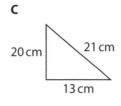
20 cm  21 cm  13 cm

**D**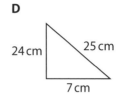
24 cm  25 cm  7 cm

**[I got ___ / 1 mark]**

 **2.** Work out the length of the unknown side in each of these triangles.

**a)**
6 cm
8 cm  $x$

**b)**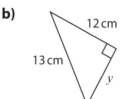
12 cm
13 cm  $y$

........................................ cm [ ___ / 3 marks]   ........................................ cm [ ___ / 3 marks]

 **3.** Work out the length of the unknown side in each of these triangles. Give your answers to 1 decimal place.

**a)**
11 cm
15 cm
$x$

**b)**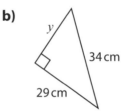
$y$
34 cm
29 cm

........................................ cm [ ___ / 3 marks]   ........................................ cm [ ___ / 3 marks]

 **4.** Point $A$ has coordinates (–1, 3). Point $B$ has coordinates (2, 8).

Work out the length of the line segment $AB$ to 3 significant figures.

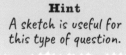

**Hint**
A sketch is useful for this type of question.

........................................ **[ ___ / 4 marks]**

 **5.** The diagram shows the dimensions of a prize-winning biscuit in a baking competition. The biscuit is in the shape of an isosceles triangle. Work out the height of the biscuit to 1 decimal place.

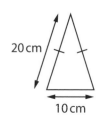
20 cm
10 cm

........................................ cm   **[ ___ / 3 marks]**

# Trigonometry 1

**1.** Work out the length of the unknown side in each of these triangles. Give your answers to 1 decimal place.

**a)**

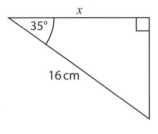

............................................ cm

**b)**

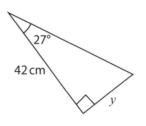

............................................ cm

**c)**

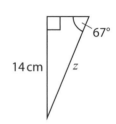

............................................ cm

**[I got ___ / 6 marks]**

**d)**

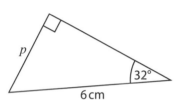

............................................ cm

**e)**

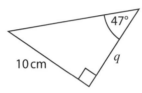

............................................ cm

**f)**

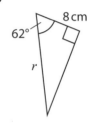

............................................ cm

**[ ___ / 6 marks]**

**2.** Work out the height of this trapezium to 3 significant figures.

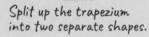

**Hint**
Split up the trapezium
into two separate shapes.

............................................ cm  **[ ___ / 3 marks]**

**3.** From where Taylor is lying on the ground, the angle of elevation of a helicopter is 26°.
The helicopter is flying at a vertical height of 1000 m above the ground.
How far is the helicopter from Taylor? Give your answer to 2 significant figures.

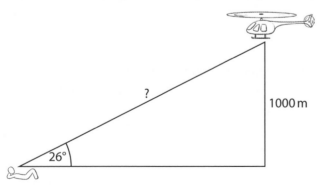

............................................ m  **[ ___ / 2 marks]**

88

# Trigonometry 2

**1.** Circle the value of sin $x$ for this triangle.

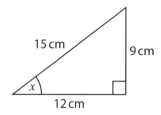

$$\frac{9}{12} \qquad \frac{9}{15} \qquad \frac{12}{15} \qquad \frac{4}{3}$$

**[I got ___ / 1 mark]**

**2.** Work out the size of angle $x$ in each of these triangles.

Write your answers to 1 decimal place.

**a)**

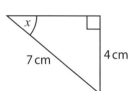

**b)**

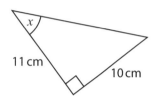

**c)**

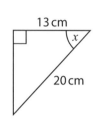

......................................... °          ......................................... °          ......................................... °

**[ ___ / 6 marks]**

**3.** Triangle $PQR$ is an isosceles triangle. Work out angle $PQR$ to 1 decimal place.

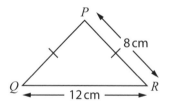

**Hint**
Split the isosceles triangle into two right-angled triangles. Be careful – angle QPR is not a right angle.

......................................... **[ ___ / 3 marks]**

**4.** A hang glider is flying at an altitude of 1.2 km when it starts its descent towards the ground.

Work out the angle of depression if the hang glider is 3 km from its landing zone.

Give your answer to 3 significant figures.

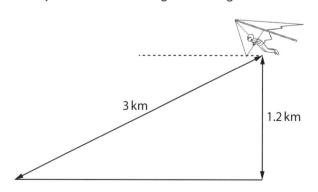

......................................... **[ ___ / 3 marks]**

# Exact values

**1.** Circle the exact value of $\cos 0°$

$0$ $\qquad$ $\dfrac{1}{2}$ $\qquad$ $\dfrac{\sqrt{3}}{2}$ $\qquad$ $1$ $\qquad$ **[I got ___ / 1 mark]**

**Grade 5**

**2.** Work out the length of the side labelled $x$ in each of these triangles.

**Hint**
Use SOHCAHTOA.

**a)**

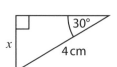

**b)**

**c)**

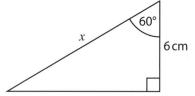

...................................... cm ...................................... cm ...................................... cm

**[ ___ / 9 marks]**

**Grade 5**

**3.** Write the value of

**a)** $\cos 45°$ ............................................... **[ ___ / 1 mark]**

**b)** $\tan 45° + \sin 30°$ ............................................... **[ ___ / 2 marks]**

**c)** $\sin 60°$ ............................................... **[ ___ / 1 mark]**

**d)** $\tan 60° - \cos 90°$ ............................................... **[ ___ / 2 marks]**

**Grade 5**

**4.** Arthur has completed a table of exact trigonometric ratios, but some of the values are incorrect.

|  | 0° | 30° | 45° | 60° | 90° |
|---|---|---|---|---|---|
| $\sin \theta$ | 0 | $\dfrac{1}{2}$ | $\dfrac{1}{\sqrt{2}}$ | $\dfrac{\sqrt{3}}{2}$ | 0 |
| $\cos \theta$ | 1 | $\dfrac{\sqrt{3}}{2}$ | $\dfrac{\sqrt{3}}{2}$ | $\dfrac{1}{2}$ | 0 |
| $\tan \theta$ | 0 | $\sqrt{3}$ | 1 | $\dfrac{\sqrt{3}}{2}$ | undefined |

**a)** Identify the incorrect values and circle them in the table. **[ ___ / 4 marks]**

**b)** For each value that you have circled, clearly write the correct values below.

............................................... **[ ___ / 4 marks]**

# Vectors

 **1.** If $\overrightarrow{OA} = \mathbf{a}$, write a vector which is parallel to $\overrightarrow{OA}$ but is three times its length.

.................................................. **[I got ___ / 1 mark]**

 **2.** If $\overrightarrow{OB} = \mathbf{b}$, write a vector which is parallel to $\overrightarrow{OB}$ but is in the opposite direction.

.................................................. **[ ___ / 1 mark]**

 **3.** $OPQR$ is a rhombus. $\overrightarrow{OP} = \mathbf{p}$ and $\overrightarrow{OR} = \mathbf{r}$

Write these vectors in terms of $\mathbf{p}$ and $\mathbf{r}$

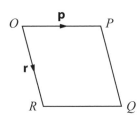

**a)** $\overrightarrow{PO}$ .................................................. **[ ___ / 1 mark]**

**b)** $\overrightarrow{OP} + \overrightarrow{PQ}$ .................................................. **[ ___ / 1 mark]**

**c)** $\overrightarrow{QO}$ .................................................. **[ ___ / 2 marks]**

 **4.** In an **irregular** quadrilateral $ABCD$, $\overrightarrow{AB} = \overrightarrow{DC}$ and $\overrightarrow{BC} = \overrightarrow{AD}$

Circle the name of quadrilateral $ABCD$

> **Hint**
> A shape is irregular if the sides and angles are not all the same.

Kite      Trapezium      Parallelogram      Square      **[ ___ / 1 mark]**

 **5.** $PQRSTU$ is a regular hexagon. $\overrightarrow{OP} = 2\mathbf{a}$, $\overrightarrow{OQ} = 3\mathbf{b}$

Write these vectors in terms of $\mathbf{a}$ and $\mathbf{b}$

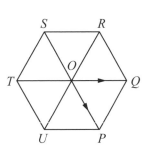

**a)** $\overrightarrow{OT}$ .................................................. **[ ___ / 1 mark]**

**b)** $\overrightarrow{PQ}$ .................................................. **[ ___ / 1 mark]**

**c)** $\overrightarrow{OU}$ .................................................. **[ ___ / 1 mark]**

**d)** $\overrightarrow{UQ}$ .................................................. **[ ___ / 1 mark]**

# Column vectors

**1.** If $\mathbf{n} = \begin{pmatrix} -2 \\ 3 \end{pmatrix}$ and $\mathbf{m} = \begin{pmatrix} -1 \\ 4 \end{pmatrix}$, work out each of these column vectors.

    **a)**   $4\mathbf{n}$ .......................................................... **[I got ___ / 1 mark]**

    **b)**   $\mathbf{n} + \mathbf{m}$ .......................................................... **[ ___ / 1 mark]**

    **c)**   $2\mathbf{m} - 3\mathbf{n}$

    .......................................................... **[ ___ / 2 marks]**

**2.** If $2\begin{pmatrix} -x \\ 3 \end{pmatrix} = \begin{pmatrix} y \\ x \end{pmatrix}$, work out the values of $x$ and $y$

    $x = $ ........................................          $y = $ ........................................ **[ ___ / 2 marks]**

**3.** Write column vectors representing **f**, **g** and **h**

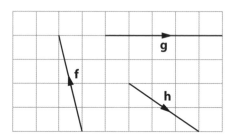

    **f** = ........................................     **g** = ........................................     **h** = ........................................ **[ ___ / 3 marks]**

**4.** If $\mathbf{p} = \begin{pmatrix} 4 \\ 3 \end{pmatrix}$ and $\mathbf{q} = \begin{pmatrix} 2 \\ -5 \end{pmatrix}$, draw a **triangle** of vectors on the grid below representing **p**, **q** and **p** + **q**

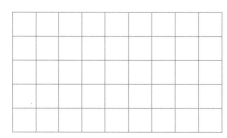

> **Hint**
> Remember to draw an
> arrow on each vector to
> indicate its direction.

    **[ ___ / 4 marks]**

**5.** In the grid shown, $\overrightarrow{OA} = \begin{pmatrix} 0 \\ 2 \end{pmatrix}$, $\overrightarrow{OB} = \begin{pmatrix} 2 \\ 4 \end{pmatrix}$ and $\overrightarrow{OD} = \begin{pmatrix} 1 \\ 1 \end{pmatrix}$

    Given that $ABCD$ is a rectangle, write the column vector that represents $\overrightarrow{OC}$

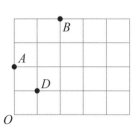

    .......................................................... **[ ___ / 2 marks]**

# Sampling

**Grade 4**

**1.** Sam wants to predict the football results for upcoming matches. He uses a list of results for matches that took place five years ago.

   **a)** What type of data is Sam using?

   ........................................................................................................................................................ **[I got ___ / 2 marks]**

   **b)** Give a reason why the data might not be reliable.

   ........................................................................................................................................................ **[ ___ / 1 mark]**

**Grade 4**

**2. a)** Write one advantage of using secondary data rather than primary.

   ........................................................................................................................................................ **[ ___ / 1 mark]**

   **b)** Write one disadvantage of using secondary data rather than primary.

   ........................................................................................................................................................ **[ ___ / 1 mark]**

**Grade 5**

**3.** 180 sixth form students want to celebrate their end-of-course exam results.

   A sample of 40 students is taken to decide how they should celebrate.

   Their preferences are shown in the table.

| Type of celebration | Frequency |
|---|---|
| Cinema trip | 11 |
| Party | 10 |
| Meal out | 11 |
| Day at funfair | 8 |

   **a)** Work out how many of the 180 students you think would like a day at the funfair.

   ........................................................................................................................................................ **[ ___ / 2 marks]**

   **b)** State one assumption that you have made in your answer to part **a**.

   ........................................................................................................................................................ **[ ___ / 1 mark]**

**Grade 5**

**4. a)** Write what is meant by a random sample.

   ........................................................................................................................................................ **[ ___ / 1 mark]**

   Harriet wants to do a questionnaire about the favourite foods of students in her school.

   She selects five of her best friends to take part.

   **b)** Identify    **i)**   the population   ........................................................ **[ ___ / 1 mark]**

                 **ii)**   the sample.   ........................................................ **[ ___ / 1 mark]**

   **c)** Give a reason why her sample might be biased.

   ........................................................................................................................................................ **[ ___ / 1 mark]**

   **d)** Write two ways that her sample can be improved.

   ........................................................................................................................................................ **[ ___ / 2 marks]**

# Organising data

**1.**

```
1 | 1  4  5  6  8
2 | 1  1  2  8  8  8  9
```

Key: 1|1 means 1.1

**Hint**
The median is the middle value when the values are in numerical order and the mode occurs most often.

For the stem-and-leaf diagram shown, write

**a)** the median

......................................................... **[I got ___ / 1 mark]**

**b)** the mode.

......................................................... **[ ___ / 1 mark]**

**2.** The times taken in minutes to travel to school each day by 20 pupils are:

```
5   25   15   6    3    5    20   16   20   9
7    3   18   21   11   10   10   17   4    8
```

Complete the grouped frequency table.

| Time (minutes) | Frequency |
|---|---|
| 0–5 | |
| 6–10 | |
| 11–15 | |
| 16–20 | |
| 21–25 | |

**[ ___ / 2 marks]**

**3.** The two-way table shows the drink choices of some people in a café.

| | Tea | Coffee | Total |
|---|---|---|---|
| **Sugar** | | 5 | |
| **No sugar** | | 7 | 10 |
| **Total** | 9 | | 21 |

**a)** Complete the values in the table. **[ ___ / 2 marks]**

**b)** How many people don't have sugar in their drink?

......................................................... **[ ___ / 1 mark]**

**4.** The back-to-back stem-and-leaf diagram shows the percentage scores obtained by a group of students in a maths test and a physics test.

```
        Physics        Maths
     6 4 1 0 0 | 5 | 2 2 3 6 8
         8 6 6 | 6 | 1 4 7 7 7 8
 4 2 2 2 1 1 1 | 7 | 8 9 9
```

Key: 0|5|2 means 50 for Physics and 52 for Maths

**Hint**
Think about what calculations you could do to help you make comparisons.

Make two comparisons between the two data sets.

......................................................................................................

......................................................................................................

......................................................... **[ ___ / 4 marks]**

# Simple charts

1.

| Vanilla | |
|---|---|
| Strawberry |  ice cream cones |
| Chocolate | ice cream cones |

**Key**

🍦 = _____ children

The incomplete pictogram shows the favourite ice cream flavours of some children.

30 children choose strawberry flavour as their favourite.

**a)** Write the number that should be written in the key.

............................................................... **[I got ___ / 1 mark]**

**b)** How many children prefer chocolate flavour?

............................................................... **[ ___ / 1 mark]**

**c)** 20 children say that vanilla is their favourite. Complete the pictogram to show this.

**[ ___ / 1 mark]**

2. The table shows how 30 people travel to work.

| Car | Walk | Bus | Train |
|---|---|---|---|
| 15 | 7 | 3 | 5 |

Draw a bar chart to show this information.

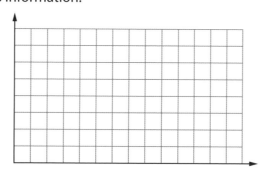

**[ ___ / 3 marks]**

3. The composite bar chart shows the sales of socks and shoes over three months.

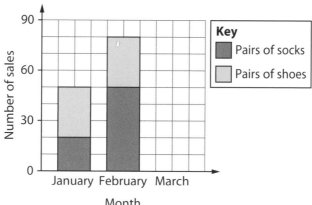

**Key**
- ▓ Pairs of socks
- ░ Pairs of shoes

**Hint**
You need to use the key to interpret the bar chart properly.

**a)** How many pairs of socks were sold in January?

............................................................... **[ ___ / 1 mark]**

**b)** In February, what was the difference between the number of sales of socks and of shoes?

............................................................... **[ ___ / 1 mark]**

**c)** In March, 50 pairs of shoes and 30 pairs of socks were sold.

Complete the composite bar chart to show this information. **[ ___ / 2 marks]**

# Pie charts

1. The pie chart shows the age groups of 200 people who took part in a survey.

   Circle the number of people who were aged 16–24

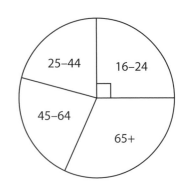

   20          25          50          90

**[I got ___ / 1 mark]**

2. The table gives information about the favourite type of books of some students.

   Complete the table and draw an accurate pie chart to show the information.

| Favourite type | Science fiction | Fantasy | Romance | Other | Total |
|---|---|---|---|---|---|
| **Frequency** | 34 | 20 | 6 | 12 | |
| **Angle** | | 100° | | | 360° |

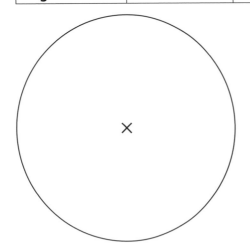

**Hint**

$$\text{Angle} = \frac{frequency}{total\ frequency} \times 360°$$

**[ ___ / 3 marks]**

3. The pie charts show some information about GCSE grades at two secondary schools.

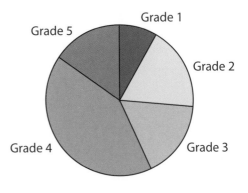

Barry says that more students achieved Grade 4 at Summerton High.

Is Barry correct? Give a reason for your answer.

........................................................................................................................................

........................................................................................................................................

**[ ___ / 2 marks]**

# Averages and spread

**1.** Write the median of this list of numbers.

| 34 | 31 | 32 | 37 | 30 | 28 | 39 |

........................................................................................ **[I got ___ / 1 mark]**

**2.** Bertrand rolled an 8-sided dice 16 times. His scores were:

| 2 | 4 | 3 | 2 | 8 | 6 | 2 | 2 |
| 7 | 1 | 1 | 2 | 4 | 6 | 8 | 6 |

**a)** Write the mode.

........................................................................................ **[ ___ / 1 mark]**

**b)** Work out the median.

........................................................................................ **[ ___ / 2 marks]**

**c)** Work out the mean.

........................................................................................ **[ ___ / 2 marks]**

**d)** Work out the range.

........................................................................................ **[ ___ / 1 mark]**

**3.** For each of these sets of data, write which would be the best average to use. Give a reason for each answer.

**a)**  blue        blue        brown        blue        brown        green

........................................................................................ **[ ___ / 2 marks]**

**b)**  1        18        21        22        23        24        65

........................................................................................ **[ ___ / 2 marks]**

**c)**  6.2        6.7        6.2        6.4        6.8        6.5        6.6

........................................................................................ **[ ___ / 2 marks]**

**4.** Written on each one of four cards is a positive number. The mean of the numbers is 6, the mode is 8 and the median is 7. Fill in the cards.

> **Hint**
> The mode must occur more than once.

........................................................................................ **[ ___ / 2 marks]**

**5.** The mean of 10 numbers is 63

The mean of four of the numbers is 51

Work out the mean of the remaining 6 numbers.

> **Hint**
> Work out the total of each set of numbers.

........................................................................................ **[ ___ / 3 marks]**

# Averages from tables

**1.** Ginger rolled a dice 20 times. Her results are shown below.

| 5 | 3 | 4 | 6 | 3 | 1 | 3 | 3 | 5 | 3 |
|---|---|---|---|---|---|---|---|---|---|
| 6 | 6 | 2 | 3 | 1 | 1 | 1 | 5 | 4 | 2 |

**a)** Complete the frequency table to show Ginger's results.

| Score on dice | Tally | Frequency |
|---|---|---|
| 1 | | |
| 2 | | |
| 3 | | |
| 4 | | |
| 5 | | |
| 6 | | |

> **Hint**
> The range is the difference between the largest and the smallest values.

[I got ___ / 2 marks]

**b)** Write   **i)**  the mode ............................................................  [ ___ / 1 mark]

**ii)** the range ............................................................  [ ___ / 1 mark]

**iii)** the median. ............................................................  [ ___ / 1 mark]

**2.** The tables show the number of goals scored by Fermat United and Gauss Town in their last 20 matches.

**Fermat United**

| Number of goals, $g$ | Frequency, $f$ |
|---|---|
| 0 | 0 |
| 1 | 12 |
| 2 | 8 |
| 3 | 0 |

**Gauss Town**

| Number of goals, $g$ | Frequency, $f$ | |
|---|---|---|
| 0 | 5 | |
| 1 | 6 | |
| 2 | 5 | |
| 3 | 4 | |

**a)** Work out the mean number of goals scored by Gauss Town.

............................................................  [ ___ / 3 marks]

The mean number of goals scored by Fermat United is 1.4

**b) i)** Circle the range of goals scored for Fermat United.

1          2          3          4          [ ___ / 1 mark]

**ii)** On average, which team scored more goals per match? Give a reason for your answer.

............................................................  [ ___ / 2 marks]

**iii)** Which team is more consistent? Give a reason for your answer.

............................................................  [ ___ / 2 marks]

# Grouped data

**1.** 100 worms are measured.

The table shows their measurements in cm.

| Length ($x$ cm) | Frequency, $f$ | Midpoint | $f \times$ midpoint |
|---|---|---|---|
| $0 < x \le 8$ | 50 | 4 | 200 |
| $8 < x \le 16$ | 30 | 12 | *360* |
| $16 < x \le 24$ | 20 | *20* | 400 |
| Total | 100 | | *960* |

$\dfrac{960}{100}$

$= 9.6$

**a)** Complete the missing values in the table. **[I got _2_/ 2 marks]**

**b)** Write the modal class. *group with highest frequency*

*~~is 200~~ $0 < x \le 8$* **[_1_/ 1 mark]**

**c)** Work out an estimate for the mean length.

_9.6_ cm **[_~~1~~2_/ 2 marks]**

**2.** 71 people take part in a 5 km race.

The table shows their finishing times in minutes.

| Time ($t$ minutes) | Frequency | m.p ~~9~~/10 (11) 17, 24 | f x mp |
|---|---|---|---|
| $20 < t \le 25$ | 10 | 22·5 | ·225 |
| $25 < t \le 30$ | 17 | 27·5 | 467·5 |
| $30 < t \le 35$ | 24 | 32·5 | 180 |
| $35 < t \le 40$ | 11 | 37·5 | 412·5 |
| $40 < t \le 45$ | 9 | 42·5 | 382·5 |
| *totals* | *71* | | 2,267·5 |

**a)** Write the class interval that contains the median.

_$35 < t \le 40$_ **[_0_/ 2 marks]**

**b)** Work out an estimate for the mean finishing time.

Give your answer to the nearest minute.

> **Hint**
> Insert extra columns in the table, as in Question 1

_3.2_ minutes **[_3_/ 3 marks]**

**c)** Give a reason why your answer to part **b** is only an estimate.

_because you don't unow the values._ **[__/ 1 mark]**

**3.** Jamie says, 'I can't estimate the mean score because I don't know the value of $y$.'

| Score ($x$) | Frequency |
|---|---|
| $0 < t \le 4$ | $3y$ |
| $4 < t \le 8$ | $7y$ |

Jamie is wrong. Work out an estimate of the mean score.

**[__/ 3 marks]**

# Scatter graphs

**1.** Write the type of correlation, if any, these pairs of events are likely to demonstrate if plotted on a scatter graph.

**a)** The number of hours listening to music against shoe size

.............................................................................. **[I got ___ / 1 mark]**

**b)** The number of builders against time taken to build a house

.............................................................................. **[ ___ / 1 mark]**

**c)** The length of a fish against its mass

.............................................................................. **[ ___ / 1 mark]**

**2.** The table shows the number of absences of some students along with their final examination scores.

| Number of absences | 0 | 2 | 5 | 10 | 17 | 20 | 25 | 30 | 35 | 40 |
|---|---|---|---|---|---|---|---|---|---|---|
| Examination score | 90 | 85 | 76 | 75 | 75 | 50 | 35 | 80 | 40 | 20 |

**a)** Draw a scatter diagram to show this data.

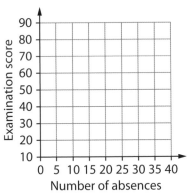

**[ ___ / 2 marks]**

**b)** One of the points is an outlier. Circle the outlier on your graph. **[ ___ / 1 mark]**

**c)** What type of correlation does the graph show?

.............................................................................. **[ ___ / 1 mark]**

**3.** The scatter graph shows the time of some bus journeys along with the number of times that the bus stopped.

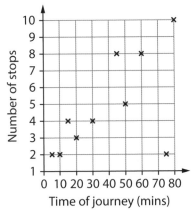

**a)** Describe the correlation between the time of a bus journey and the number of stops.

.............................................................................. **[ ___ / 1 mark]**

**b)** Write the coordinates of the outlier.

.............................................................................. **[ ___ / 1 mark]**

# Lines of best fit

**1.** The scatter graph shows the relationship between the age and height of a child.

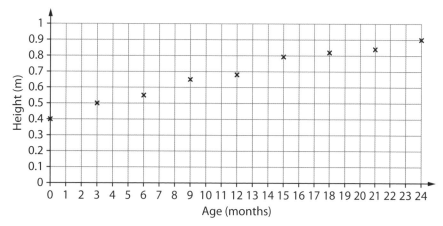

a) Draw a line of best fit on the scatter graph. **[I got ___ / 1 mark]**

b) Use the line of best fit to estimate the height of the child at 20 months old.

...................................................... m **[ ___ / 1 mark]**

c) Give a reason why it would not be sensible to use the line of best fit to estimate the height of the child at 36 months old.

.................................................................................................................. **[ ___ / 1 mark]**

**2.** A scatter graph shows that there is positive correlation between the number of sandcastles made at a beach and the number of electric fans sold in a shop.

Trevor says that the increase in the number of sandcastles causes an increase in the number of sales of electric fans. Make a criticism of Trevor's statement.

.................................................................................................................. **[ ___ / 1 mark]**

**3.** The scatter graph shows the relationship between the gradient of some hills and the speed of some cyclists.

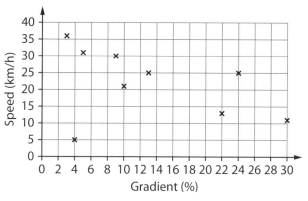

> **Hint**
> Remember an outlier does not follow the same trend as the rest of the data.

a) Ignoring the outlier, draw a line of best fit on the scatter graph. **[ ___ / 1 mark]**

b) Use the line of best fit to estimate the gradient of a hill if a cyclist is travelling at 15 km/h.

.................................................... **[ ___ / 1 mark]**

c) Marta uses the line of best fit to estimate that a cyclist travelling up a hill with 40% gradient should be travelling at a speed of 5 km/h. Make a criticism of Marta's assumption.

.................................................................................................................. **[ ___ / 1 mark]**

# Time series

**1.** Describe the general trend in this time series graph.

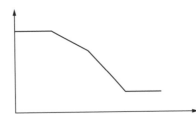

........................................................................ **[I got ___ / 1 mark]**

**2.** The table shows the monthly profits made by a shop over a period of seven months.

| Month | Jan | Feb | Mar | Apr | May | Jun | July |
|---|---|---|---|---|---|---|---|
| Profit (£) | 3000 | 3500 | 4200 | 4500 | 4000 | 5000 | 6000 |

**a)** Construct a time series graph for this data.

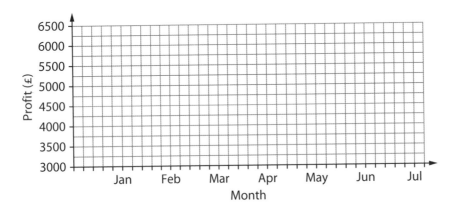

**[ ___ / 2 marks]**

**b)** Describe the general trend of the data. ............................................ **[ ___ / 1 mark]**

**c)** Comment on why the graph might be misleading.

........................................................................ **[ ___ / 1 mark]**

**3.** The time series graph shows the attendance figures at a football ground over an eight-week period.

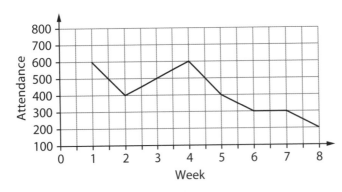

**a)** Describe the general trend of the data. ............................................ **[ ___ / 1 mark]**

**b)** In which two weeks was attendance at its highest?

........................................................................ **[ ___ / 1 mark]**

**c)** Use the general trend to predict the attendance in Week 9

........................................................................ **[ ___ / 1 mark]**

# Theoretical probability

**Grade 2** **1.** A fair, 6-sided dice is rolled. Write the probability for each of these events.

**a)** Rolling a 1 ...................................................... **[I got ___ / 1 mark]**

**b)** Rolling an odd number ...................................................... **[ ___ / 1 mark]**

**c)** Rolling a 3 or a 5 ...................................................... **[ ___ / 1 mark]**

**Grade 2** **2.** The circular spinner has eight sectors of equal size. A probability scale is shown.

Write the position (A, B or C) shown on the probability scale that matches each statement.

**a)** The spinner lands on a multiple of 2 ...................................................... **[ ___ / 1 mark]**

**b)** The spinner lands on an integer. ...................................................... **[ ___ / 1 mark]**

**c)** The spinner lands on a number greater than 2

...................................................... **[ ___ / 1 mark]**

**Grade 3** **3.** A bag contains some blue balls and red balls in the ratio 1 : 2

If a ball is randomly taken from the bag, what is the probability that it is red? Circle your answer.

$\dfrac{1}{2}$ $\qquad$ $\dfrac{1}{3}$ $\qquad$ $\dfrac{2}{3}$ $\qquad$ 2 $\qquad$ **[ ___ / 1 mark]**

**Grade 3** **4.** A card is chosen at random from five cards.

E    A        S    P

> **Hint**
> Convert the decimals into fractions.

The probability of choosing a card containing the letter S is 0.2

The probability of choosing a card containing the letters S or A is 0.6

**a)** On the blank card, write the letter that it contains. **[ ___ / 1 mark]**

**b)** A card is chosen at random from the five cards. What is the probability that the letter on the chosen card is contained in the word PASTA?

...................................................... **[ ___ / 1 mark]**

**Grade 4** **5.** The probability of winning a particular game is $x$

The probability of losing the game is $x + \dfrac{1}{2}$

The game cannot be drawn. Work out the value of $x$

> **Hint**
> The probabilities must add up to 1. Use your algebra skills.

...................................................... **[ ___ / 2 marks]**

# Mutually exclusive events

**Grade 3**

**1.**

| Event A = rolling a 3 on a dice | Event B = rolling a 6 on a dice |

Event A = rolling a 3 on a dice    Event B = rolling a 6 on a dice

Event C = rolling an even number on a dice    Event D = getting a head in a coin toss

Event E = getting a tail in a coin toss

Which of these pairs of events are mutually exclusive?

Write **yes** if they are. Write **no** if they are not.

**a)** Event A and Event B ............................................................ **[I got __ / 1 mark]**

**b)** Event B and Event C ............................................................ **[ __ / 1 mark]**

**c)** Event D and Event E ............................................................ **[ __ / 1 mark]**

**Grade 3**

**2.** The probability that it will snow on a particular day is 0.1

Write the probability that it will not snow.

............................................................ **[ __ / 1 mark]**

**Grade 3**

**3.** In a prize draw, raffle tickets are numbered 1 to 50

Write the probability that the winning ticket number

**a)** is 39 ............................................................ **[ __ / 1 mark]**

**b)** is not a multiple of 8

............................................................ **[ __ / 2 marks]**

**c)** contains at least one 3

............................................................ **[ __ / 2 marks]**

**Grade 4**

**4.** A bag contains white, yellow, pink and orange counters.

The table shows the probabilities of selecting each colour of counter from the bag.

| Colour | White | Yellow | Pink | Orange |
|---|---|---|---|---|
| Probability | 0.3 | 0.15 | 0.26 | |

**a)** Work out the probability of selecting an orange counter.

............................................................ **[ __ / 2 marks]**

**b)** What is the probability of **not** selecting a white or a pink counter?

............................................................ **[ __ / 2 marks]**

**c)** There are 200 counters in the bag. Work out how many are yellow.

............................................................ **[ __ / 2 marks]**

# Possibility spaces

**1.** Two fair 6-sided dice are rolled. This possibility space shows all of the possible outcomes.

**Hint**
There are 36 possible outcomes.

Write the probability that the dice show

a) a 4 on both dice .................................................... **[I got ___ / 1 mark]**

b) a 4 on just one of the dice .................................. **[ ___ / 1 mark]**

c) one even number and one odd number. .................................. **[ ___ / 1 mark]**

**2.** Two 4-sided spinners are spun and their scores are added together.

a) Complete the possibility space grid.

Spinner 1

Spinner 2

Spinner 1

| + | 1 | 2 | 3 | 4 |
|---|---|---|---|---|
| 1 | 2 |   |   |   |
| 2 |   |   |   |   |
| 3 |   |   |   |   |
| 4 |   |   |   |   |

Spinner 2

**[ ___ / 2 marks]**

b) Write the probability that the total is less than 4

.................................................... **[ ___ / 1 mark]**

c) Sally asks Jacob to predict what the total will be when she spins the two spinners. Jacob says, 'I think the total will be 4'. Make a criticism of Jacob's prediction.

.................................................................................................................... **[ ___ / 2 marks]**

**3.** Jason can either win or lose a game.

a) List the possible outcomes when he plays three games.

.................................................... **[ ___ / 2 marks]**

He is equally likely to win or to lose each game.

b) Work out the probability that he wins at least one of the games.

.................................................... **[ ___ / 2 marks]**

# Probability experiments

**Grade 3**

**1.** When dropped onto a hard surface, a drawing pin will either land 'pin up' or 'pin down'.

**a)** Sheena is doing an experiment to find out which is the more likely outcome. She drops a drawing pin 50 times and records the results. Complete the table.

|  | Pin up | Pin down |
| --- | --- | --- |
| **Frequency** | 35 |  |
| **Relative frequency** |  | 0.3 |

**[I got ___ / 2 marks]**

**b)** She then drops the drawing pin a further 100 times and it lands 'pin up' 60 times. Using her results from this second experiment, give an estimate of the probability of a drawing pin landing 'pin down'.

.............................................................................................. **[ ___ / 1 mark]**

**Grade 3**

**2.** In an experiment, the relative frequency of a biased coin landing on heads is found to be 0.2

If the coin landed on heads four times, how many times was the coin thrown?

> **Hint**
> Convert the decimal into a fraction.

.............................................................................................. **[ ___ / 2 marks]**

**Grade 4**

**3.** The frequency tree shows the outcomes of 40 people who took a driving test.

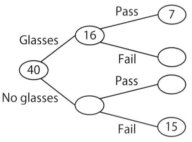

**a)** Complete the frequency tree. **[ ___ / 2 marks]**

**b)** Write the probability that a person chosen at random wears glasses and passes the test.

.............................................................................................. **[ ___ / 1 mark]**

**Grade 4**

**4.** Zebedee plays six games of chess and wins $\frac{1}{3}$ of them. He plays eight games of draughts and loses 25% of them.

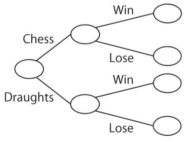

**a)** Complete the frequency tree. **[ ___ / 2 marks]**

**b)** A game is chosen at random. Write the probability that the game is chess and he loses.

.............................................................................................. **[ ___ / 1 mark]**

# Expected results

**1.** The probability of a particular bus being late is 0.3

Circle how many times you would expect the bus to be late in 20 randomly chosen days.

3          6          9          12          **[I got ___ / 1 mark]**

**2.** In a bag of sweets, 20 are purple, 16 are green, 24 are red and 20 are black.

**a)** A sweet is taken from the bag at random. Work out the probability that the sweet is red.

.................................................................................................... **[ ___ / 1 mark]**

**b)** 20 sweets are randomly selected from the bag. How many do you expect to be red?

.................................................................................................... **[ ___ / 2 marks]**

**3.** The probability of a report being submitted on time is 0.85

**a)** Out of 60 reports, how many would you expect to be submitted on time?

.................................................................................................... **[ ___ / 2 marks]**

**b)** Out of 170 reports, 160 are submitted on time.
Is this more or fewer than what you would have expected? Give a reason for your answer.

.................................................................................................... **[ ___ / 2 marks]**

**4.** An unbiased 8-sided dice has the numbers 1, 2, 2, 3, 3, 4, 4 and 4 on its faces.

**a)** If the dice is rolled once, what is the probability that it will land on 4?

.................................................................................................... **[ ___ / 1 mark]**

**b)** If the dice is rolled 40 times, how many times would you expect it to land on 3?

.................................................................................................... **[ ___ / 2 marks]**

**c)** The dice is rolled repeatedly and lands on the number 4 a total of 36 times.
Estimate how many times the dice was rolled.

.................................................................................................... **[ ___ / 2 marks]**

**5.** The sides of a biased 5-sided spinner are numbered 1, 2, 3, 4 and 5
The table shows the probabilities of landing on each number.

| Number | 1 | 2 | 3 | 4 | 5 |
|---|---|---|---|---|---|
| Probability | 0.2 | 0.4 | 0.16 | 0.13 | |

If the spinner is spun 2500 times, how many times would you expect it to land on 5?

.................................................................................................... **[ ___ / 3 marks]**

# Tree diagrams

**1.** The tree diagram shows the probabilities of a baseball player hitting a ball.

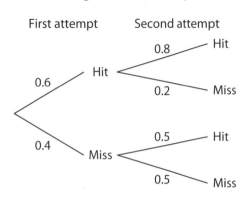

First attempt    Second attempt

**Hint**
Multiply along the branches.

Work out the probability that the player misses on both attempts. Circle your answer.

0.02          0.2          0.7          0.9          **[I got ___ / 1 mark]**

**2.** Maryam plays one game of bridge and one game of cribbage.

The probability that Maryam will win at bridge is $\frac{2}{3}$

The probability that Maryam will win at cribbage is $\frac{5}{8}$

**a)** Complete the probability tree diagram.

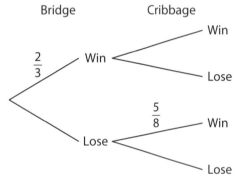

Bridge          Cribbage

**[ ___ / 2 marks]**

**b)** Work out the probability that Maryam wins both games.

**[ ___ / 2 marks]**

**3.** Chen answers two questions. What is the probability that she gets the second question correct?

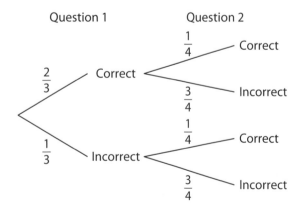

Question 1          Question 2

**[ ___ / 1 mark]**

# Set notation

**1.** 60 people were asked if they read fiction or non-fiction books.
20 said they read only non-fiction. Five said they don't read either. 28 people said they read fiction only. Complete the Venn diagram.

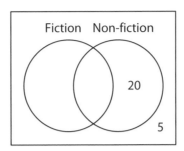

**[I got ___ / 2 marks]**

**2.** There are 79 students in a college. 44 study art. 12 study both art and music. 11 don't study either. Complete the Venn diagram.

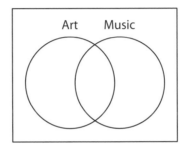

> **Hint**
> Fill in the intersection first.

**[ ___ / 4 marks]**

**3.** In the Venn diagram, $A \cap B = \{7, 9\}$

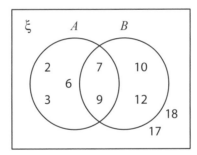

Write the numbers that are in the set

**a)** $A \cup B$ ............................................................ **[ ___ / 1 mark]**

**b)** $A'$ ............................................................ **[ ___ / 1 mark]**

**4.** $\xi = \{1, 2, 4, 8, 16, 25, 27, 64\}$, $A = \{$square numbers$\}$, $B = \{$cube numbers$\}$

**a)** Draw a Venn diagram for this information.

**[ ___ / 4 marks]**

**b)** Write the numbers that are in the set $A \cap B$

............................................................ **[ ___ / 1 mark]**

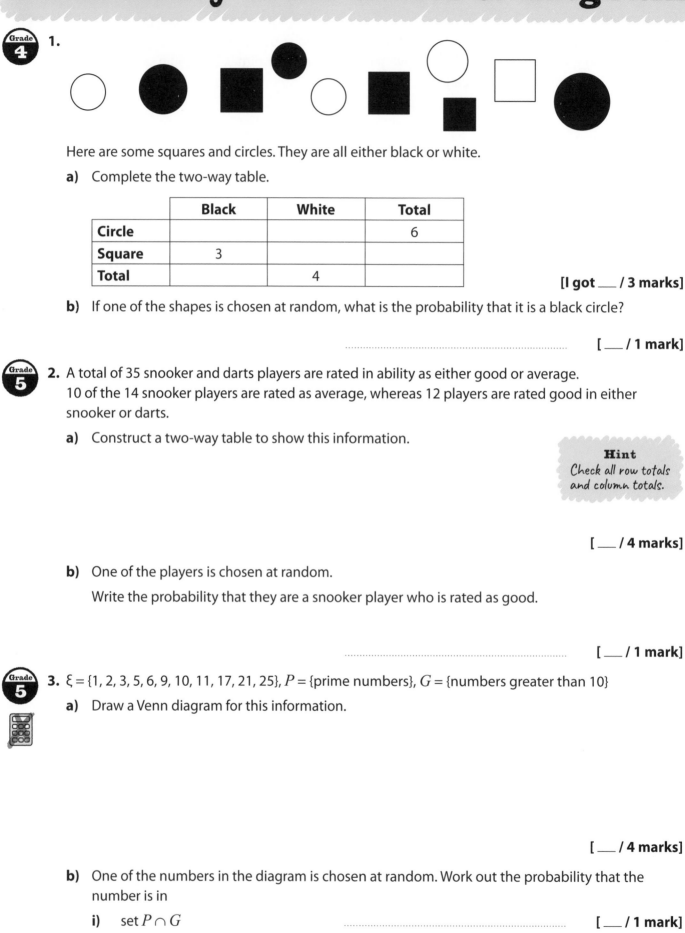

**Grade 4** 1.

Here are some squares and circles. They are all either black or white.

a) Complete the two-way table.

| | Black | White | Total |
|---|---|---|---|
| **Circle** | | | 6 |
| **Square** | 3 | | |
| **Total** | | 4 | |

[I got ___ / 3 marks]

b) If one of the shapes is chosen at random, what is the probability that it is a black circle?

............................................................................................ [ ___ / 1 mark]

**Grade 5** 2. A total of 35 snooker and darts players are rated in ability as either good or average.
10 of the 14 snooker players are rated as average, whereas 12 players are rated good in either snooker or darts.

a) Construct a two-way table to show this information.

**Hint**
Check all row totals and column totals.

[ ___ / 4 marks]

b) One of the players is chosen at random.

Write the probability that they are a snooker player who is rated as good.

............................................................................................ [ ___ / 1 mark]

**Grade 5** 3. $\xi$ = {1, 2, 3, 5, 6, 9, 10, 11, 17, 21, 25}, $P$ = {prime numbers}, $G$ = {numbers greater than 10}

a) Draw a Venn diagram for this information.

[ ___ / 4 marks]

b) One of the numbers in the diagram is chosen at random. Work out the probability that the number is in

i) set $P \cap G$ ............................................ [ ___ / 1 mark]

ii) set $G'$ ............................................ [ ___ / 1 mark]

iii) set $P$ only. ............................................ [ ___ / 1 mark]

# Paper 1 Non-Calculator

## Foundation Tier

Time allowed: 1 hour 30 minutes

- Answer **all** questions.
- In all calculations, show clearly how you work out your answers.
- Diagrams are **NOT** accurately drawn, unless indicated.
- You must **not** use a calculator.

**[I got ___ / 80 marks]**

---

**1.** Circle the value represented by the digit 5 in the number 74.54

       0.05        0.5        5        50        **[I got ___ / 1 mark]**

**2.** Round 267 to the nearest 10. Circle your answer.

       300        270        260        200        **[ ___ / 1 mark]**

**3.** Circle the percentage equal to $\frac{3}{10}$

       0.03%        0.3%        3%        30%        **[ ___ / 1 mark]**

**4.** Circle the number equal to the reciprocal of 0.5

       2        $\frac{1}{2}$        –2        5        **[ ___ / 1 mark]**

**5. a)** Write the following as algebraic expressions.

    **i)**   6 less than $f$

                                         **[ ___ / 1 mark]**

    **ii)**  Twice as much as $d$

                                         **[ ___ / 1 mark]**

**b)** Given that $T = 2h - k$, write the value of $T$ when $h = 4$ and $k = 3$

                                         **[ ___ / 2 marks]**

**6.** Constance claims the proportion shaded in shape $A$ is greater than the proportion shaded in shape $B$.

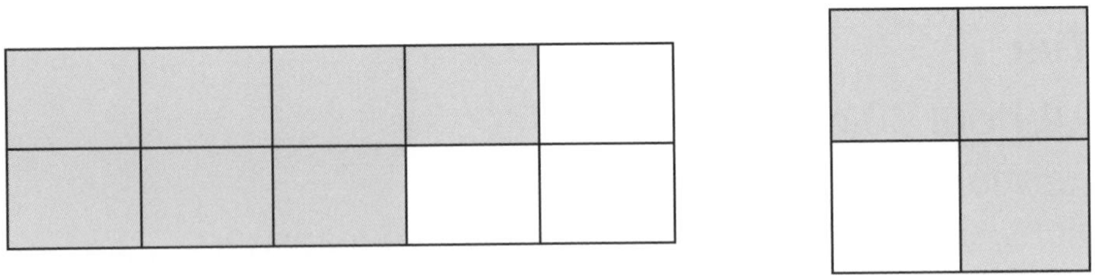

$A$

$B$

Is Constance correct? Give a reason for your answer.

.................................................................................................................................... [ __ / 2 marks]

**7.** The pictogram shows the amount of time that Ethan spends on his mobile phone from Monday to Thursday during one week.

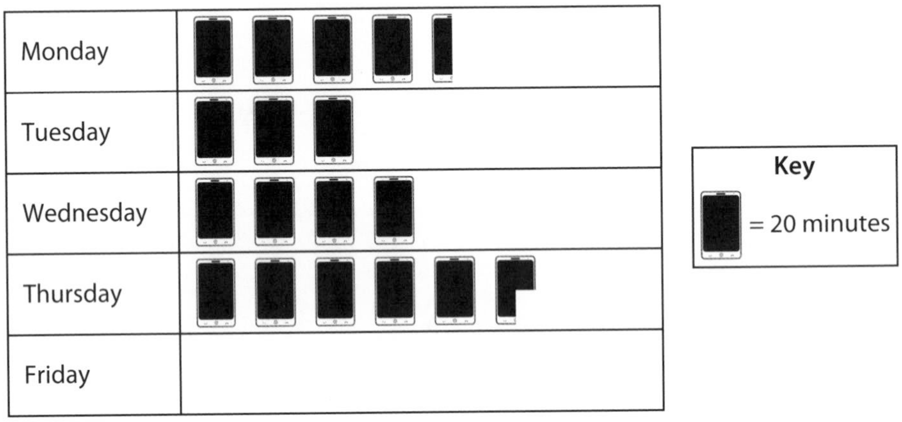

| | |
|---|---|
| Monday | |
| Tuesday | |
| Wednesday | |
| Thursday | |
| Friday | |

| Key |
|---|
| = 20 minutes |

Over the five-day period from Monday to Friday, Ethan spends a total of 7 hours 45 minutes on his mobile phone.

Complete the pictogram. [ __ / 3 marks]

**8.** A bag contains 180 g of flour.

Tom uses $\frac{2}{3}$ of the flour in a recipe.

How much flour does Tom use?

........................................................................g   [ __ / 2 marks]

**9.** Circle the value of $2^0$

$\qquad\qquad$ 0 $\qquad$ 1 $\qquad$ 2 $\qquad$ $\frac{1}{2}$ $\qquad\qquad$ [ __ / 1 mark]

**10.** Work out

**a)** $3.2 \times 3.6$

.................................................................. [ __ / 3 marks]

Further practice & support: Q6 p.9/13; Q7 p.95; Q8 p.10; Q9 p.15; Q10 p.8

**b)** $4.2 \div 0.07$

....................................................................................  **[ ___ / 2 marks]**

**11. a)** *AB* and *CD* are parallel lines.

Write the value of angle $x$. Give a reason for your answer.

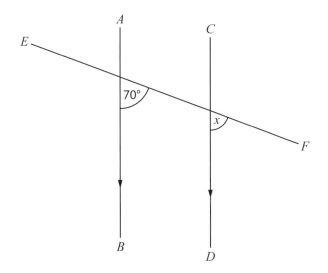

$x =$ .......................................° Reason: ........................................... **[ ___ / 2 marks]**

**b)** Work out the value of angle $y$. Show your working in full.

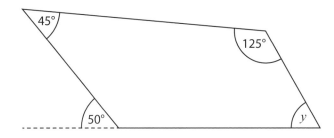

$y =$ ...........................................° **[ ___ / 3 marks]**

**12. a)** Give a reason why this calculation is incorrect.

$3 + 4 \times 5 = 7 \times 5 = 35$

....................................................................................  **[ ___ / 1 mark]**

**b)** Work out $2 + 4 \times 6^2$

....................................................................................  **[ ___ / 2 marks]**

Further practice & support: Q10 p.8; Q11 p.63; Q12 p.2

**13.** In a music exam, Faye scores 24 out of 30 for a performance and 21 out of 25 for sight-reading. Which is the better score? Show your working in full.

[ ___ / 3 marks]

**14.** Given that $276 \times 52 = 14\,352$, write down the value of

**a)** $27.6 \times 5.2$

[ ___ / 1 mark]

**b)** $2.76 \times 52\,000$

[ ___ / 1 mark]

**c)** $14.352 \div 0.276$

[ ___ / 1 mark]

**15. a)** Write 360 as a product of its prime factors.
Give your answer in index notation.

[ ___ / 2 marks]

**b)** Rosie says 360 is divisible by 15. Using your answer to part **a**, state whether or not Rosie is correct. Give a reason for your answer.

[ ___ / 1 mark]

**16.** A monthly magazine subscription costs £3.99 per month.
An annual subscription to the magazine costs £42
Zain buys an annual subscription.
Jenny buys the magazine monthly for 12 months.
Work out who gets the magazine cheaper.
Show your working in full.

[ ___ / 3 marks]

Further practice & support: Q13 p.50; Q14 p.1; Q15 p.17; Q16 p.8

**17.** There are 25 pencils in a box. The pencils are red, blue or yellow.

Five of the pencils are red.

There are three times as many blue pencils as yellow pencils.

Write the ratio of red pencils to blue pencils to yellow pencils.

Give your answer in its simplest form.

.............................................................................................. **[ __ / 3 marks]**

**18.** Chang makes some patterns out of matchsticks.

Pattern 1          Pattern 2                    Pattern 3

**a)**  In the space below, draw Pattern 4

**[ __ / 1 mark]**

**b)  i)**  Circle the number of matchsticks in the 7th pattern.

9          11          13          15          **[ __ / 1 mark]**

**ii)**  Work out how many matchsticks there will be in the $n$th pattern.

.......................................................................... **[ __ / 2 marks]**

**c)**  Darren says, 'Pattern 100 will contain 201 matchsticks.'

Give a reason why Darren is correct.

.......................................................................................................................... **[ __ / 1 mark]**

**19. a)** Estimate $\frac{12.4 \times 107.3}{0.48}$

Show your working.

.................................................................... [ ___ / 2 marks]

**b)** Is your answer to part **a** an overestimate or an underestimate?

Give a reason for your answer.

.................................................................... [ ___ / 1 mark]

**20.** Solve the equation $3(2x - 3) = 39$

$x =$ .................................................... [ ___ / 2 marks]

**21.** Yootha eats $\frac{3}{8}$ of a pizza. Zoe eats $\frac{1}{2}$ of the remaining pizza.

Work out the fraction of the pizza that has been eaten.

.................................................................... [ ___ / 3 marks]

**22.** Each of these equations matches to one of the graphs.

$$y = \frac{1}{x} \qquad y = x^2 \qquad y = x^3 \qquad y = x$$

Write the correct equation below each graph.

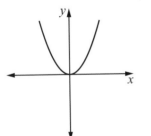 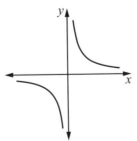 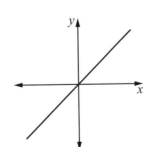 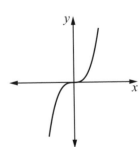

.................... .................... .................... ....................

[ ___ / 2 marks]

Further practice & support: Q19 p.5; Q20 p.27; Q21 p.11/12; Q22 p.44

**23.** The density of oak is 700 kg/m³.

A particular piece of oak has a volume of 0.5 m³.

Work out the mass of the piece of the oak. Give your answer in grams.

.................................................... g    **[ ___ / 3 marks]**

**24.** Each of the cards below contains a number.

| −3 | | 1 | 4 | 7 | | 32 |

The mode of the numbers is −3

The mean of the numbers is 7

**a)** Fill in the correct numbers on each of the blank cards.

**[ ___ / 2 marks]**

**b)** Circle the value of the range of the numbers.

29            35            14            32            **[ ___ / 1 mark]**

**c)** Which average (mode, mean or median) is most suitable for these numbers? Give your reasoning.

**[ ___ / 3 marks]**

**25.** Circle the exact value of cos 60°.

0            $\frac{1}{2}$            $\frac{\sqrt{3}}{2}$            1            **[ ___ / 1 mark]**

Further practice & support: Q23 p.56; Q24 p.97; Q25 p.90

**26.** Sonny and Blair each draw a triangle.

Sonny's triangle has angles of sizes 45°, 60° and $x$°.

Blair's triangle has angles of sizes 60°, 75° and $y$°.

Sonny says that the two triangles must be congruent. Blair disagrees.

Who is correct? Give a reason for your answer.

.................................................................................................................................................................. **[ ___ / 3 marks]**

**27.** A small bag of sweets costs 75 pence.

A large bag costs 90 pence.

The large bag contains 25% more sweets than the small bag.

Which bag is better value?

You must show your working.

................................................................................ **[ ___ / 3 marks]**

**28.** Simplify $(2 \times 10^4) \times (2 \times 10^2)^2$

Give your answer in standard form.

................................................................................ **[ ___ / 2 marks]**

**29.** A piece of wood is cut into two pieces, A and B.

The ratio of the length of A to the length of B is 2 : 7, and B is 60 cm longer than A.

Work out the length piece of wood before it was cut.

................................................................................cm     **[ ___ / 3 marks]**

# End of paper

Further practice & support: Q26 p.71; Q27 p.50; Q28 p.20; Q29 p.52

# Paper 2 Calculator

## Foundation Tier

Time allowed: 1 hour 30 minutes
- Answer **all** questions.
- In all calculations, show clearly how you work out your answers.
- Diagrams are **NOT** accurately drawn, unless indicated.
- You must have a calculator for this paper.

**[I got ___ / 80 marks]**

---

**1.** Change 25 cm to mm. Circle your answer.

       0.25 mm        2.5 mm        250 mm        2500 mm        **[I got ___ / 1 mark]**

**2.** Circle the next prime number after 23

       25        27        29        31        **[ ___ / 1 mark]**

**3.** Circle the decimal equal to 45%.

       0.045        0.45        4.5        45.0        **[ ___ / 1 mark]**

**4.** Solve the equation $x - 5 = 12$. Circle your answer.

       −17        −7        7        17        **[ ___ / 1 mark]**

**5.** Write these numbers in order of size.

Start with the smallest number.

       0.7        0.07        0.707        0.077

**[ ___ / 1 mark]**

Further practice & support: Q1 p.60; Q2 p.17; Q3 p.13; Q4 p.26; Q5 p.1

**6.** Here is a list of numbers.

$$2 \quad 6 \quad 9 \quad 15 \quad 24 \quad 27$$

For each statement below, write **True** or **False**. Give your reasons.

**a)** There are no cube numbers in the list.

.................................................................................................................................... [ ___ / 1 mark]

**b)** There is exactly one factor of 12 in the list.

.................................................................................................................................... [ ___ / 1 mark]

**c)** There are exactly two triangular numbers in the list.

.................................................................................................................................... [ ___ / 1 mark]

**7.** Astrid orders two bike lights and a bike lock online.

Each bike light costs £7.20

The bike lock costs £32.50

Astrid pays using a £50 gift voucher.

She thinks she will have more than £3 left of her voucher.

Is Astrid correct? Show your working.

.................................................................................................... [ ___ / 3 marks]

**8.** A map has a scale 1 cm to 5 km.

A cycle path is 34.5 km long.

Work out how long the cycle path is on the map.

....................................................cm    [ ___ / 2 marks]

Further practice & support: Q6 p.16; Q7 p.8; Q8 p.61

**9.** Ingrid has attempted to expand and simplify the expression below, but she has made a mistake.

$$3 + 2(x + 4)$$
$$= 5(x + 4)$$
$$= 5x + 20$$

Make a criticism of Ingrid's working.

.................................................................................................................... [ ___ / 1 mark]

**10.** A baby elephant standing on the ground exerts a force of 900 N. The area of its feet is 200 cm².

What is the pressure of the elephant's feet on the ground in N/cm²?

...................................................................N/cm²    [ ___ / 2 marks]

**11.** The table shows the population of a village between 1950 and 2010

| Year | 1950 | 1960 | 1970 | 1980 | 1990 | 2000 | 2010 |
|------|------|------|------|------|------|------|------|
| Population | 1270 | 1180 | 1165 | 1402 | 1812 | 1815 | 1970 |

**a)** Construct a time series graph for this data.

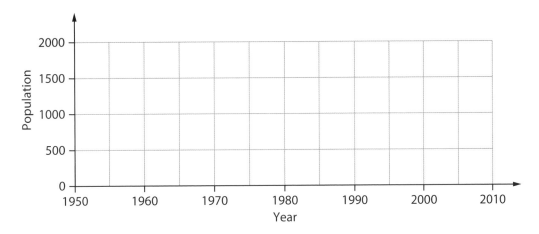

[ ___ / 2 marks]

**b)** Describe the general trend of the data.

.................................................................................................... [ ___ / 1 mark]

Further practice & support: Q9 p.29; Q10 p.56; Q11 p.102

**12.** Work out $\dfrac{1.6 + (-0.35)}{3.27 - (-1.3)}$

Write your answer to 2 decimal places.

.................................................................... [ __ / 2 marks]

**13.** Simplify

a) $-5t + 6t - 2t$

.................................................................... [ __ / 1 mark]

b) $y \times y \times y$

.................................................................... [ __ / 1 mark]

c) $x^2 + x^2 + x^2$

.................................................................... [ __ / 1 mark]

d) $\dfrac{4z^2}{2z}$

.................................................................... [ __ / 2 marks]

**14.** 40% of spectators at a lacrosse match are supporting the away team.

Circle the ratio of away supporters to home supporters.

$1:1.5$      $1:40$      $1.5:1$      $40:1$      [ __ / 1 mark]

**15.** A puzzle cube has a volume of 450 cm³.

Work out its surface area.

Give your answer to the nearest whole number and include the units.

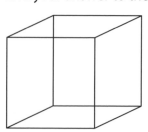

.................................................................... [ __ / 4 marks]

Further practice & support: Q12 p.7; Q13 p.22; Q14 p.51; Q15 p.78

**16. a)** On the axes below, draw a straight line graph for the data in the table.

| $x$ | -2 | 0 | 1 | 2 | 4 |
|---|---|---|---|---|---|
| $y$ | 5 | 3 | 2 | 1 | -1 |

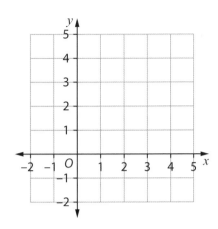

[ __ / 2 marks]

**b)** Write the equation of the straight line in the form $y = mx + c$.

.................................................................................... [ __ / 3 marks]

**c)** If the line is extended, will the point with coordinates (97, −100) lie on the line? Show your working.

.................................................................................... [ __ / 2 marks]

**17.** The table shows the preferred pieces of 60 players in a board game.

| Piece | Dog | Car | Iron | Hat | Boat |
|---|---|---|---|---|---|
| Frequency | 15 | 25 | 5 | 7 | |

Complete the frequency table and draw a pie chart to illustrate the data.

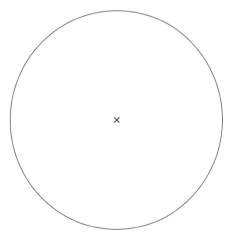

[ __ / 5 marks]

Further practice & support: Q16 p.40; Q17 p.96

**18.** The recipe below makes 12 pancakes.

      100 g flour

      2 large eggs

      300 ml milk

Delia has 130 g flour, 3 large eggs and 350 ml of milk.

Delia says that she has enough ingredients to make 15 pancakes.

Is Delia correct? Show working to support your answer.

[ __ / **3 marks**]

**19.** Factorise fully

    **a)** $4x + 12x^2$

[ __ / **2 marks**]

    **b)** $x^2 + 5x - 6$

[ __ / **2 marks**]

**20.** In a sale, a sign states that everything is 20% off the original price.

The sale price of a coat is £44.80

The coat label shows the original price was £53.76

Is the sign correct? Give your reasoning.

[ __ / **3 marks**]

**21.** $a = 2^2 \times 3^2$ and $b = 2^2 \times 3^5$

Frank says that $ab = 4^4 \times 9^7$. Give a reason why Frank is incorrect.

[ __ / **1 mark**]

**22.** Work out the bearing of $A$ from $B$. Circle your answer.

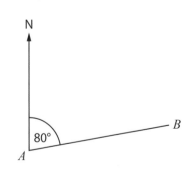

    080°        80°        100°        260°        [ __ / **1 mark**]

Further practice & support: Q18 p.51; Q19 p.30/32; Q20 p.55; Q21 p.15; Q22 p.64

**23.** In a test, class 3A has a median score of 45 and a range of 20

For the same test, class 3B has a median score of 39 and a range of 8

Compare the data for the two classes.

..........................................................................................................................................................

.......................................................................................................................................................... [ __ / 2 marks]

**24.** The distance from Nairobi to Mombasa is 440 km.

A car travels from Nairobi to Mombasa in 4 hours and 20 minutes.

Work out the average speed of the car in km/h to 1 decimal place.

.........................................................................km/h    [ __ / 3 marks]

**25.** The diameter of Earth is 12 742 000 m.

The diameter of Jupiter is $1.429\,84 \times 10^8$ m.

Sebastian claims that the diameter of Jupiter is over 1000 times greater than the diameter of Earth.

Is Sebastian correct? Give a reason for your answer.

..........................................................................................................................................................

..........................................................................................................................................................

.......................................................................................................................................................... [ __ / 3 marks]

**26.** The tree diagram shows the probability of a competitor hitting the bullseye on two separate attempts.

**a)** Complete the missing probabilities on the tree diagram.    [ __ / 2 marks]

**b)** Work out the probability of hitting the bullseye with both attempts.

.......................................................................................................... [ __ / 2 marks]

Further practice & support: Q23 p.97; Q24 p.56; Q25 p.20; Q26 p.108

**27.** Andrew has some jelly beans. 25% of them are white, $\frac{1}{6}$ are red and the rest are green.

Work out the ratio of red jelly beans to green jelly beans in its simplest form.

............................................................................................. [ __ / 3 marks]

**28. a)** A number $x$ is rounded to 2 decimal places. The result is 0.87

Complete the error interval for $x$.

.......................................... $\leq x <$ .......................................... [ __ / 2 marks]

**b)** A number $y$ is truncated to a whole number. The result is 7

Complete the error interval for $y$.

.......................................... $\leq y <$ .......................................... [ __ / 2 marks]

**29.** The radius, $r$, of a cylinder, is equal to its height.

The volume of the cylinder is 1000 cm³. Work out the value of $r$ to 1 decimal place.

.......................................................................cm    [ __ / 3 marks]

**30.** A bird spots a worm on the ground. The worm is 50 m away from the bird on an angle of depression of 40°. Work out the vertical height of the bird above the ground at this instant.

Give your answer to 2 significant figures.

.......................................................................m    [ __ / 3 marks]

## End of paper

Further practice & support: Q27 p.52; Q28 p.6; Q29 p.81; Q30 p.88

# Paper 3 Calculator 🖩

**Foundation Tier**

Time allowed: 1 hour 30 minutes
- Answer **all** questions.
- In all calculations, show clearly how you work out your answers.
- Diagrams are **NOT** accurately drawn, unless indicated.
- You must have a calculator for this paper.

[I got ___ / 80 marks]

---

**1.** Work out the value of $4^5$. Circle your answer.

       20            45          625          1024        **[I got ___ / 1 mark]**

**2.** Work out the fraction that is equivalent to 0.03. Circle your answer.

    $\frac{3}{1000}$         $\frac{3}{100}$         $\frac{3}{10}$         $\frac{1}{30}$       **[ ___ / 1 mark]**

**3.** Change 1500 millilitres to litres. Circle your answer.

    1.5 litres       15 litres       150 000 litres       1 500 000 litres     **[ ___ / 1 mark]**

**4.** Simplify $3t + t - 6t$. Circle your answer.

      $-10t$         $-2t$         $2t$         $10t$       **[ ___ / 1 mark]**

**5.** Circle the number that is both a square number and a cube number.

      4           8         64         100       **[ ___ / 1 mark]**

Further practice & support: Q1 p.14; Q2 p.13; Q3 p.60; Q4 p.22; Q5 p.14

**6.** During a game of chess, the number of black pieces and white pieces on the board is in the ratio 3 : 2

If there 25 pieces on the board, work out how many of them are white.

[ ___ / 2 marks]

**7.** A bag contains 28 balls. Three of the balls are yellow and four of the balls are blue. The rest are other colours.

A ball is chosen from the bag at random.

Jonas says that the probability of the ball being neither yellow nor blue is 75%.

Is Jonas correct? Show your working.

[ ___ / 3 marks]

**8.** Fred cooks some jacket potatoes. He turns the oven on at 10:30 am. After 20 minutes, he puts the potatoes in the oven. The potatoes cook for $1\frac{1}{4}$ hours.

At what time are the potatoes cooked? Circle your answer.

12:05          12:15          11:45          11:50          [ ___ / 1 mark]

**9.** Vicky needs to buy some protractors, sticky tape and pencil sharpeners. The prices for each item are given in the table.

| | |
|---|---|
| Protractors | 12p each or buy five and get the sixth free |
| Sticky tape | 24p per roll or 10 rolls for £2 |
| Pencil sharpeners | 18p each or buy one and get second half-price |

Work out how much money Vicky will have to spend to get exactly 25 of each item.

[ ___ / 4 marks]

Further practice & support: Q6 p.52; Q7 p.103; Q8 p.59; Q9 p.50

**10.** Mr Trick writes down all of the integers from 11 to 30 on the board.

He asks a student to choose one of the integers.

Assuming that every number has an equal of chance of being picked, write down the probability that the student chooses

**a)** 25

.................................................................................... [ __ / **1 mark**]

**b)** 1

.................................................................................... [ __ / **1 mark**]

**c)** a multiple of 3

.................................................................................... [ __ / **1 mark**]

**d)** a two-digit number.

.................................................................................... [ __ / **1 mark**]

**11. a)** Part of a Fibonacci-type sequence is 3, 4, 7, …

Work out the next two terms.

.................................................................................... [ __ / **1 mark**]

**b)** Part of a geometric sequence is 24, 12, 6, 3, …

Describe the term-to-term rule.

.................................................................................... [ __ / **1 mark**]

**c)** An arithmetic sequence has first term 7 and third term 3

Work out the 4th term of the sequence.

.................................................................................... [ __ / **2 marks**]

**12.** Two people take 19 working days to decorate a house.

Work out how long it would take four people.

..............................................................days [ __ / **2 marks**]

**13.** Work out the value of $x$ for the function machine shown. Circle your answer.

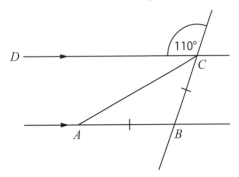

$-2$      $2$      $13$      $40$      [ __ / **1 mark**]

**14.** Lines $AB$ and $DC$ are parallel.

$ABC$ is an isosceles triangle with $AB = BC$.

Work out the size of angle $BCA$. Show your working and give your reasons.

...................................................°   [ __ / **3 marks**]

**15. a)** Work out $\dfrac{\sqrt{5^2 + 41}}{3.4^3}$. Give all the digits on your calculator display in your answer.

....................................................   [ __ / **2 marks**]

**b)** Write your answer to part **a** to three significant figures.

....................................................   [ __ / **1 mark**]

**16.** Using a ruler and pair of compasses, construct the perpendicular from the point $P$ to the line segment $AB$.

Show all of your construction lines.

[ __ / **3 marks**]

Further practice & support: Q13 p.25; Q14 p.63; Q15 p.2/4; Q16 p.85

**17.** $A = \{p, e, a, r, s\}$

$B = \{o, r, a, n, g, e, s\}$

List the elements of the set

**a)** $A \cap B$

.................................................... [ __ / 1 mark]

**b)** $A \cup B$

.................................................... [ __ / 1 mark]

**18.** The radius of the semicircle shown is 6 cm.

Work out the perimeter of the semicircle, giving your answer to 2 decimal places.

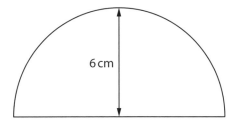

6 cm

...................................................cm    [ __ / 3 marks]

**19.** Here is a square-based pyramid.

The side length of the base is 4.8 cm. The perpendicular height of each triangular face is 5.3 cm.

Work out the perpendicular height of the pyramid. Give your answer to 3 significant figures.

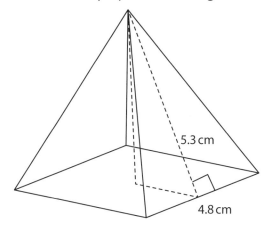

5.3 cm

4.8 cm

...................................................cm    [ __ / 3 marks]

Further practice & support: Q17 p.109; Q18 p.76; Q19 p.87

**20.** Oliver is on holiday in the US and wants to buy a designer T-shirt.

The T-shirt cost $30 in the US and £24 in the UK.

The exchange rate for pounds to US dollars is £1 = $1.31

Where would you advise him to buy the T-shirt? You must show your working.

[ ___ / 2 marks]

**21.** In a cinema audience, the ratio of the number of people who brought a mobile phone with them to the number of people who did not is 3 : 1

90% of the people with phones remembered to switch them off.

84 mobile phones were left on during the film.

Work out the total number of people in the cinema audience.

You must show your working.

[ ___ / 3 marks]

**22. a)** Work out the lowest common multiple (LCM) of 36 and 80

[ ___ / 2 marks]

**b)** Work out the highest common factor (HCF) of 80 and 24. Circle your answer.

8          16          80          240          [ ___ / 1 mark]

Further practice & support: Q20 p.57; Q21 p.55; Q22 p.18

**23.** The grouped frequency table shows the waiting times of some people in a doctor's surgery.

| Time ($t$ minutes) | Frequency |
|---|---|
| $0 < t \leq 10$ | 13 |
| $10 < t \leq 20$ | 7 |
| $20 < t \leq 30$ | 12 |
| $30 < t \leq 40$ | 28 |
| $40 < t \leq 50$ | 7 |

**a)** Write down the class interval that contains the median.

........................................................................................................ [ __ / 1 mark]

**b)** Sheena says that the mode is 7. Write down the error that Sheena has made.

........................................................................................................ [ __ / 1 mark]

**c) i)** Estimate the mean waiting time, giving your answer to 1 decimal place.

...............................................................minutes   [ __ / 4 marks]

**ii)** Give a reason why your answer to part **i** is only an estimate.

........................................................................................................ [ __ / 1 mark]

**24.** A rectangle has length $x$ and width $y$.

**a)** Circle the expression for the perimeter of the rectangle.

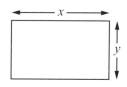

$x + y$          $xy$          $2x + 2y$          $4xy$

[ __ / 1 mark]

**b)** The length of the rectangle is twice the width.

The area of the rectangle is $20\,\text{cm}^2$.

Work out the length of the rectangle.

...............................................................cm   [ __ / 4 marks]

Further practice & support: Q23 p.99; Q24 p.73

**25.** $ABC$ is an isosceles triangle with $AC = BC = 15$ cm and $AB = 6$ cm.

Work out the size of angle $CAB$, giving your answer to 1 decimal place.

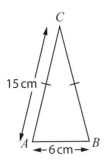

.............................................................°    [ __ / 3 marks]

**26. a)** Solve the inequality $2x - 5 \leq 7 - x$

..........................................................    [ __ / 2 marks]

**b)** Represent your answer to part **a** on a number line.

[ __ / 1 mark]

**c)** $n$ is an integer such that $-3 < 3n \leq 9$

Write down all of the possible values of $n$.

..........................................................    [ __ / 2 marks]

**27.** A savings account in a bank earns 3% compound interest per year.

An initial amount of money is deposited in the account and, at the end of one year, there is a total of £711.22 in the bank account.

How much money was initially deposited in the account?

..........................................................    [ __ / 2 marks]

Further practice & support: Q25 p.89; Q26 p.37; Q27 p.55

**28.** Reuben wants to solve this pair of simultaneous equations for $x$ and $y$.

$$2x - 3y = 16$$
$$5x - 3y = 31$$

He has decided to add the equations first.

**a)** Give a reason why adding the equations is not a good idea.

..................................................................................................................................................... **[ __ / 1 mark]**

**b)** Solve the simultaneous equations for $x$ and $y$.

$x =$ ................................................. $y =$ ................................................. **[ __ / 3 marks]**

**29.** Describe fully the single transformation that maps shape $A$ onto shape $B$.

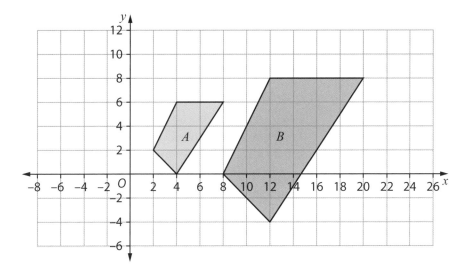

..................................................................................................................................................... **[ __ / 3 marks]**

## End of paper

# Guided answers

*A correct final answer automatically scores all the marks, unless specified otherwise.*

## Page 1, Place value

**1.** 90 124
*1 mark for correct answer.*
**2. a** 200    **b** 20 000    **c** $\frac{2}{10}$ or 0.2
*1 mark for each correct answer.*
**3. a** >    **b** =    **c** <
*1 mark for each correct answer.*
**4.** 7.054, 7.405, 7.45, 7.504
*2 marks for correct order; 1 mark for any three in correct order.*
**5. a** $67.9 \times 1000 = 67\,900$    **b** $0.9 \div 100 = 0.009$
*1 mark for each correct answer.*
**6.** £8.50 ÷ 10 = £0.85, so 1 packet costs 85p.
*1 mark for 85p circled.*
**7. a** $4.5 \times 19.2 = 4.5 \times 192 \div \mathbf{10} = 864 \div \mathbf{10} = 86.4$
You could also estimate: $4.5 \times 19.2 \approx 5 \times 20 \approx 100$, which is close to 86.4
**b** $450 \times 0.0192 = 4.5 \times \mathbf{100} \times 192 \div \mathbf{10\,000}$
$= 864 \times \mathbf{100} \div \mathbf{10\,000} = 8.64$
You could also estimate: $450 \times 0.0192 \approx 500 \times 0.02 \approx 10$, which is close to 8.64
**c** You know that $864 \div 4.5 = 192$,
so $8.64 \div 0.45 = \frac{864 \div \mathbf{100}}{4.5 \div \mathbf{10}} = 192 \div \mathbf{10} = 19.2$
You could also estimate: $8.64 \div 0.45 \approx 10 \div 0.5 \approx 20$, which is close to 19.2
*1 mark for each correct answer.*

## Page 2, Order of operations

**1. a** $2 + 3 \times 9 = 2 + 27 = 29$
**b** $24 \div (6 - 2) \times 5 = 24 \div 4 \times 5 = 30$
**c** $10 - 3^2 = 10 - 9 = 1$
*1 mark for each correct answer.*
**2.** $20 - (5 - 2 + 6)$ is the correct calculation.
*1 mark for correct answer circled.*
**3. a** $(12 - 4 \times 2)^3 = (12 - 8)^3 = 4^3 = 64$
**b** $\frac{4 \times 5^2}{4 \times 5 \div 2} = \frac{4 \times 25}{10} = \frac{100}{10} = 10$
**c** $5 \times \sqrt{50 - 1} + 6 \times 3 = 5 \times \sqrt{49} + 6 \times 3$
$= 5 \times 7 + 6 \times 3$
$= 35 + 18 = 53$
*1 mark for each correct answer.*
**4. a** $\frac{2 \times 36 + 18}{20 - 12} = \frac{90}{8} = \frac{45}{4}$ or 11.25
**b** $\left(\frac{3}{5}\right)^3 + 9 \div 3 = \frac{27}{125} + 3 = \frac{402}{125}$ or 3.216
**c** $\sqrt{7.29} \times 1000 = 2.7 \times 1000 = 2700$
*1 mark for each correct answer.*
**5.** There are a number of ways to explain this. Two examples of correct explanations would be:
Eva is correct because you calculate $3^2$, which is 9, then multiply by 2, so $2 \times 9 = 18$
Eva is correct. Bavan made the mistake of multiplying before squaring, whereas Eva squared before multiplying.
*1 mark for a correct, detailed explanation.*

## Page 3, Rounding and truncating

**1. a** 258    **b** 260    **c** 300
*1 mark for each correct answer.*
**2. a** 20    **b** 19.9    **c** 19.90
*1 mark for each correct answer.*
**3. a** 8    **b** 8.2    **c** 8.26
*1 mark for each correct answer.*
**4.** $3.66 \times 9 = 32.94 \approx 33\,\text{m}^2$
*1 mark for correct multiplication; 1 mark for rounding.*
**5.** 3000 ÷ 310 = 9.677, so the jug will fill 9 whole glasses.
*1 mark for correct division; 1 mark for truncating to an integer.*
**6.** $18.93 \times 7.5 = 141.975$, so Mark earns £141.98 a day.
$22.17 \times 6.5 = 144.105$, so Kwamé earns £144.11 a day.
The difference in their pay is £144.11 − £141.98 = £2.13 a day.
*1 mark for Mark's pay; 1 mark for Kwamé's pay; 1 mark for the difference. Total 3 marks.*

## Page 4, Significant figures

**1.** 0.050 28 = 0.050 to 2 sf
The first significant figure is the first non-zero digit (in this case, 5). This means the two significant figures here are 5 and 0. Since the 0 is followed by a 2, you do not round up.
*1 mark for 0.050 circled.*
**2. a** 20 190    **b** 20 200
   **c** 20 000    **d** 20 000
*1 mark for each correct answer.*
**3.** Side length $= \sqrt{40} = 6.32455532 = 6.32$ cm to 3 sf
*1 mark for square rooting; 1 mark for 6.32*
**4. a** $\frac{4.56 \times 2.89}{12.1 - 0.56} = 1.141\,975\,737$
**b** $1.141\,975\,737 = 1.1$ to 2 sf
*1 mark for each correct answer.*
**5.** Shirley has rounded 0.065 29 to 2 dp instead of 2 sf.
The correct answer is 0.065
*1 mark for a correct explanation.*

## Page 5, Estimation

**1.** $2.84 \times 19.3 \approx 3 \times 20 \approx 60$
*1 mark for correct answer circled. Round both numbers to 1 sf; both round up in this case.*
**2.** $\frac{317 + 48.6}{9.683} \approx \frac{300 + 50}{10} \approx \frac{350}{10} \approx 35$
*1 mark for rounding to 1 sf; 1 mark for correct answer.*
**3.** $\frac{2.67 \times 1.36}{0.11 + 0.42} \approx \frac{3 \times 1}{0.1 + 0.4} \approx \frac{3}{0.5} \approx 6$
*1 mark for rounding to 1 sf; 1 mark for correct answer.*
**4.** Number of fish at start of January ≈ 1000
Increase ≈ 20 fish per day
Five months ≈ 5 × 30 ≈ 150 days
Number of fish after five months ≈ 150 × 20 + 1000 ≈ 4000
*1 mark for rounding rate of increase to 1 sf; 1 mark for correct calculation for the number of fish after five months; 1 mark for correct answer. Total 3 marks.*
**5.** Number of portions sold ≈ 100
Sale price per portion ≈ £9.00

Cost per portion ≈ £3.00
Profit per portion ≈ £9.00 – £3.00 ≈ £6.00
Total profit ≈ £6.00 × 100 ≈ £600
*1 mark for rounding portions, sale price and cost to 1 sf;*
*1 mark for a profit calculation; 1 mark for correct answer.*
*Total 3 marks.*
*Note that you could also find the total estimated sale price*
*(£900) and subtract the total estimated cost (£300) to get*
*the total estimated profit.*

6. Distance driven ≈ 400 km
Average speed ≈ 80 km/h
Time driving ≈ $\frac{400}{80}$ ≈ 5 hours
Time for whole journey ≈ 5 hours 30 minutes (including the break)
Time of arrival is roughly 2 pm (8.30 am + $5\frac{1}{2}$ hours).
*1 mark for rounding distance and speed to 1 sf;*
*1 mark for finding the time taken; 1 mark for correct answer. Total 3 marks.*

## Page 6, Error intervals

1. The smallest number this could be is 5.25, since 5.25 is the smallest number that rounds to 5.3 to 1 dp.
*1 mark for correct answer of 5.25*

2. 13.5 ≤ L < 14.5
*1 mark for 13.5; 1 mark for 14.5*

3. a 105 ≤ p < 115    b 107.5 ≤ p < 112.5
c 109.5 ≤ p < 110.5
*1 mark for each correct minimum; 1 mark for each correct maximum.*

4. a 4.665 ≤ x < 4.675    b 4500 ≤ x < 5500
*1 mark for each correct minimum; 1 mark for each correct maximum.*

5. 245 ≤ l < 255
*1 mark for correct minimum and maximum; 1 mark for correct interval notation.*

6. Sienna can see a truncation to 1 dp, so the error interval is 1.8 ≤ x < 1.9
*1 mark for correct error interval circled.*

## Page 7, Calculating with negative numbers

1. a January    b –1 – (–5) = 4 °C
c 8 – (–5) = 13 °C
*1 mark for each correct answer.*

2. a 2 + (–5) = –3    b (–48) ÷ (–6) = 8
c (–3)² = (–3) × (–3) = 9
*1 mark for each correct answer.*

3. a 5 + (–3) × 4 = 5 + (–12) = –7
*1 mark for –12; 1 mark for correct answer.*
b (8 – 10) × 4 – (–10) = (–2) × 4 – (–10) = –8 – (–10) = 2
*1 mark for –8; 1 mark for correct answer.*

4. $\frac{-14 + (-10)}{4 - 10} = \frac{-24}{-6} = 4$
*1 mark for 4 circled.*

5. Total spend = £257.50
Bank balance = £241 – £257.50 = –£16.50
Thomas must pay in £100 + £16.50 = £116.50 to get the balance up to £100
*1 mark for subtracting the spend from £241; 1 mark for –£16.50 or £16.50 overdrawn; 1 mark for final answer of £116.50. Total 3 marks.*

## Page 8, Calculating with decimals

1. a
```
   2.906
 + 8.310
  11.216
     1
```
*1 mark for lining up the digits correctly in a column;*
*1 mark for correct answer.*

b
```
  ¹²⁵₁.043
 - 17.820
   7.223
```
*1 mark for lining up the digits correctly in a column;*
*1 mark for correct answer.*

2. a
```
      74
 ×    26
     444
 + 1480
    1924
```
Since 74 × 26 = 1924,
7.4 × 0.26 = 1924 ÷ 10 ÷ 100 = 1.924
*1 mark for multiplying 74 × 26 to get 1924; 1 mark for correct answer.*

b 17.12 ÷ 0.8 = 171.2 ÷ 8
```
    2 1.4
 8 ⟌17¹1.³2
```
171.2 ÷ 8 = 21.4
*1 mark for dividing 171.2 ÷ 8; 1 mark for correct answer.*

c $\frac{1.9 + 7.62}{9 - 8.3} = \frac{9.52}{0.7} = \frac{95.2}{7}$
```
    1 3. 6
 7 ⟌9²5.⁴2
```
$\frac{95.2}{7} = 13.6$
*1 mark for getting correct numerator and denominator;*
*1 mark for dividing 95.2 ÷ 7; 1 mark for correct answer.*
*Total 3 marks.*

3. £55.65 ÷ 7 = £7.95
```
    7. 9 5
 7 ⟌55.⁶6³5
```
*1 mark for attempting to divide; 1 mark for correct answer.*

4. By estimating, 14.5 × 2.6 ≈ 15 × 3 ≈ 45. Alex's answer is not even close.
*1 mark for a correct explanation.*

## Page 9, Introduction to fractions

1. $\frac{1}{4} > \frac{1}{5}$
Giving them a common denominator, $\frac{1}{4} = \frac{5}{20}$ and $\frac{1}{5} = \frac{4}{20}$
You can see $\frac{1}{4}$ is bigger.
Alternatively, you can say that $\frac{1}{4}$ must be bigger as one whole is split into four parts. Each part will be bigger than if the whole was split into five parts.
You can also show this by shading $\frac{1}{4}$ (horizontally) and $\frac{1}{5}$ (vertically) on the diagram:

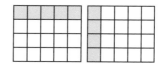

*1 mark for a correct explanation.*

**2.** Giving each fraction a common denominator of 24,

$\frac{3}{4} = \frac{18}{24}$, $\frac{2}{3} = \frac{16}{24}$, $\frac{5}{8} = \frac{15}{24}$ and $\frac{7}{12} = \frac{14}{24}$

You can now put them in order by comparing the

numerators and you have $\frac{7}{12}, \frac{5}{8}, \frac{2}{3}, \frac{3}{4}$

*2 marks for all correct, 1 mark for three out of four correct.*

**3. a i** $1\frac{2}{5} = \frac{7}{5}$

*1 mark for correct answer.*

   **ii** $3\frac{2}{4} = 3\frac{1}{2} = \frac{7}{2}$. Alternatively, $3\frac{2}{4} = \frac{14}{4} = \frac{7}{2}$

*1 mark for simplifying $\frac{2}{4}$ or $\frac{14}{4}$; 1 mark for correct answer.*

**b. i** $\frac{17}{9} = 1\frac{8}{9}$

*1 mark for correct answer.*

   **ii** $\frac{92}{40} = \frac{23}{10} = 2\frac{3}{10}$. Alternatively, $\frac{92}{40} = 2\frac{12}{40} = 2\frac{3}{10}$

*1 mark for simplifying $\frac{92}{40}$ or $\frac{12}{40}$; 1 mark for correct answer.*

**4.** Dave has $2\frac{1}{3} = \frac{7}{3} = \frac{56}{24}$ bottles left.

Lizzie has $\frac{19}{8} = \frac{57}{24}$ bottles left.

$\frac{57}{24} > \frac{56}{24}$, so Lizzie has more.

Alternatively, Lizzie has $\frac{19}{8} = 2\frac{3}{8} = 2\frac{9}{24}$ bottles left.

Dave has $2\frac{1}{3} = 2\frac{8}{24}$ bottles left.

$2\frac{9}{24} > 2\frac{8}{24}$, so Lizzie has more.

*1 mark for converting $2\frac{1}{3}$ to an improper fraction (or for converting $\frac{19}{8}$ to a mixed number); 1 mark for writing both fractions with a common denominator (such as 24); 1 mark for a correct comparison and conclusion. Total 3 marks.*

## Page 10, Proportions of amounts

**1. a** $\frac{1}{5}$ of $45 = 45 \div 5 = 9$

  **b** 30% of $180 = 180 \div 10 \times 3 = 54$

  **c** $\frac{5}{7}$ of $14 = 14 \div 7 \times 5 = 10$

  **d** 10% of $50 = 5$

    So, 60% of $50 = 5 \times 6 = 30$

    1% of $50 = 0.5$

    So, 2% of $50 = 2 \times 0.5 = 1$

    62% of $50 = 30 + 1 = 31$

*1 mark for each correct calculation; 1 mark for each correct answer.*

**2.** 10% of £2460 = £246

So, 5% of £2460 = £123

15% of £2460 = £246 + £123 = £369

*1 mark for correct answer circled. Note the question asks for the bonus only, not the earnings + bonus, and remember $15\% = \frac{15}{100}$*

**3.** 10% of $90 = 9$

So, 110% of $90 = 90 + 9 = 99$

$\frac{8}{7}$ of $84 = 84 \div 7 \times 8 = 96$

Since $99 > 96$, 110% of 90 is bigger than $\frac{8}{7}$ of 84

*1 mark for finding 110% of 90; 1 mark for finding $\frac{8}{7}$ of 84; 1 mark for a correct conclusion. Total 3 marks.*

**4.** $\frac{3}{8}$ of £7200 = £7200 $\div 8 \times 3 = £2700$

*1 mark for correct calculation; 1 mark for correct answer.*

**5.** Rock climbing: 25% of $48 = 48 \div 4 = 12$

Raft building: $\frac{5}{12}$ of $48 = 48 \div 12 \times 5 = 20$

Kayaking: $48 - 12 - 20 = 16$ children

*1 mark for the number who choose rock climbing; 1 mark for the number who choose raft building; 1 mark for the number who choose kayaking. Total 3 marks.*

## Page 11, Calculating with fractions 1

**1.** 4

*1 mark for correct answer.*

**2. a** $\frac{1}{3} \times \frac{2}{5} = \frac{2}{15}$

*1 mark for correct answer.*

  **b** $\frac{3}{7} \times \frac{14}{9} = \frac{\overset{1}{\cancel{3}} \times \overset{2}{\cancel{14}}}{\underset{1}{\cancel{7}} \times \underset{3}{\cancel{9}}} = \frac{1 \times 2}{1 \times 3} = \frac{2}{3}$

*1 mark for multiplying; 1 mark for the simplified answer.*

**3. a** $\frac{3}{4} \div \frac{1}{11} = \frac{3}{4} \times \frac{11}{1} = \frac{33}{4} = 8\frac{1}{4}$

*1 mark for turning into multiplication; 1 mark for correct answer in improper fraction or mixed number form.*

  **b** $\frac{6}{5} \div \frac{7}{10} = \frac{6}{5} \times \frac{10}{7} = \frac{6 \times \overset{2}{\cancel{10}}}{\underset{1}{\cancel{5}} \times 7} = \frac{6 \times 2}{1 \times 7} = \frac{12}{7} = 1\frac{5}{7}$

*1 mark for writing a correct multiplication; 1 mark for correct, simplified answer in improper fraction or mixed number form.*

**4.** $16 \div \frac{2}{3} = \frac{16}{1} \times \frac{3}{2} = \frac{\overset{8}{\cancel{16}} \times 3}{1 \times \underset{1}{\cancel{2}}} = \frac{8 \times 3}{1 \times 1} = \frac{24}{1} = 24$ days

*1 mark for writing a division and turning into a correct multiplication; 1 mark for correct answer.*

**5.** $\frac{1}{9}$ of $30 = \frac{1}{9} \times 30 = \frac{30}{9} = \frac{10}{3}$ m or $3\frac{1}{3}$ m

*1 mark for multiplying; 1 mark for correct simplified answer (improper fraction or mixed number).*

**6.** $\frac{1}{4}$ of $\frac{3}{10} = \frac{1}{4} \times \frac{3}{10} = \frac{3}{40}$

*1 mark for $\frac{3}{40}$ circled. Note you need to multiply the numerators and multiply the denominators.*

**7.** Area of triangle $= \frac{1}{2} \times 1\frac{1}{5} \times \frac{6}{5} = \frac{1}{2} \times \frac{6}{5} \times \frac{6}{5} = \frac{18}{25}$ cm$^2$

This is the area of the rectangle.

Length of rectangle $= \frac{18}{25} \div \frac{2}{5} = \frac{18}{25} \times \frac{5}{2} = \frac{\overset{9}{\cancel{18}} \times \overset{1}{\cancel{5}}}{\underset{5}{\cancel{25}} \times \underset{1}{\cancel{2}}} = \frac{9 \times 1}{5 \times 1}$

$= \frac{9}{5}$ cm or $1\frac{4}{5}$ cm

*1 mark for writing a correct multiplication; 1 mark for writing a division and turning into a correct multiplication; 1 mark for correct, simplified answer (improper fraction or mixed number). Total 3 marks.*

## Page 12, Calculating with fractions 2

**1. a** $\frac{1}{3} + \frac{1}{5} = \frac{5 + 3}{15} = \frac{8}{15}$

*1 mark for finding a common denominator; 1 mark for correct answer.*

  **b** $\frac{2}{9} + \frac{5}{6} = \frac{4}{18} + \frac{15}{18} = \frac{19}{18}$ or $1\frac{1}{18}$

*1 mark for finding a common denominator; 1 mark for correct answer.*

  **c** $1\frac{7}{8} + 2\frac{3}{4} = \frac{15}{8} + \frac{11}{4} = \frac{15}{8} + \frac{22}{8} = \frac{37}{8}$ or $4\frac{5}{8}$

*1 mark for converting mixed numbers to improper fractions; 1 mark for finding a common denominator; 1 mark for correct answer. Total 3 marks.*

**2. a** $\frac{7}{9} - \frac{1}{2} = \frac{14 - 9}{18} = \frac{5}{18}$

*1 mark for finding a common denominator; 1 mark for correct answer.*

  **b** $3\frac{1}{6} - 2\frac{3}{4} = \frac{19}{6} - \frac{11}{4} = \frac{38}{12} - \frac{33}{12} = \frac{5}{12}$

*1 mark for converting mixed numbers to improper fractions; 1 mark for finding a common denominator; 1 mark for correct answer. Total 3 marks.*

**3.** Janet is not correct. She has added the numerators and the denominators. She should have found a common denominator and then added the numerators only.

*1 mark for a correct explanation.*

**4.** $\frac{1}{8} + \frac{2}{3} = \frac{3+16}{24} = \frac{19}{24}$

$1 - \frac{19}{24} = \frac{24}{24} - \frac{19}{24} = \frac{5}{24}$

*1 mark for finding a common denominator of 24; 1 mark for adding to get $\frac{19}{24}$; 1 mark for correct answer. Total 3 marks.*

**5.** $2\frac{4}{5} - \frac{7}{8} + 1\frac{1}{20} = \frac{14}{5} - \frac{7}{8} + \frac{21}{20} = \frac{112}{40} - \frac{35}{40} + \frac{42}{40} = \frac{119}{40}$ m or $2\frac{39}{40}$ m

*1 mark for converting mixed numbers to improper fractions; 1 mark for finding a common denominator; 1 mark for correct answer. Total 3 marks.*

**6.** $\frac{3}{4} - \frac{1}{3} = \frac{9-4}{12} = \frac{5}{12}$

*1 mark for finding a common denominator; 1 mark for correct answer.*

## Page 13, Fractions, decimals, percentages

**1. a** $0.4 = \frac{4}{10} = \frac{2}{5}$    **b** $6\% = 0.06$    **c** $\frac{1}{8} = 12.5\%$

*1 mark for correct answer.*

**2. a** $\frac{6}{5} = 1\frac{1}{5} = 120\%$

*1 mark for for correct answer circled.*

**b** $0.035 = \frac{35}{1000} = \frac{7}{200}$

*1 mark for correct answer.*

**c** $3.6\% = 0.036$

*1 mark for correct answer.*

**3.** Convert everything to a percentage.

$0.3 = 30\%$, $\frac{1}{3} = 33.\dot{3}\%$, $\frac{16}{50} = \frac{32}{100} = 32\%$

The order is 0.3, $\frac{16}{50}$, $\frac{1}{3}$, 34%.

*1 mark for converting everything to a percentage (or everything to a decimal, or everything to a fraction with a common denominator), condone one mistake; 2 marks for correct order (1 mark for three out of four correct). Total 3 marks.*

**4.** $\frac{7}{20} = \frac{35}{100} = 35\%$, $\frac{1}{5} = 20\%$

$35\% + 20\% = 55\%$

$100\% - 55\% = 45\%$ play an album.

*1 mark for converting both fractions to a percentage; 1 mark for subtracting from 100%; 1 mark for correct answer. Total 3 marks.*

**5.** Lin's class: $\frac{6}{25} = \frac{24}{100} = 24\%$

Jay's class: $\frac{8}{32} = \frac{1}{4} = \frac{25}{100} = 25\%$

Lin is not correct. Jay's class has a (slightly) higher proportion of students who read fantasy books.

*1 mark for finding either 24% or 25% or for giving both fractions with a common denominator; 1 mark for a complete, correct explanation.*

## Page 14, Powers and roots

**1. a** $4^2 = 16$    **b** $2^3 = 8$

**c** $\sqrt{49} = 7$    **d** $\sqrt[3]{27} = 3$

*1 mark for each correct answer.*

**2. a** $2 \times \sqrt{9 + 16} + 6^2 = 2 \times \sqrt{25} + 36 = 2 \times 5 + 36$

$= 10 + 36 = 46$

*1 mark for $\sqrt{25} = 5$ and $6^2 = 36$ first; 1 mark for multiplying before adding; 1 mark for correct answer. Total 3 marks.*

**b** $3^4 - 6 \times \sqrt[3]{8} + 50 \div 5^2 = 81 - 6 \times 2 + 50 \div 25$

$= 81 - 12 + 2 = 71$

*1 mark for $3^4 = 81$, $\sqrt[3]{8} = 2$ and $5^2 = 25$ first; 1 mark for multiplying and dividing before adding and subtracting; 1 mark for correct answer. Total 3 marks.*

**3.** Side length: $\sqrt{121} = 11$ cm

Perimeter: $4 \times 11 = 44$ cm

*1 mark for side length of 11 cm; 1 mark for correct perimeter.*

**4. a** $\frac{\sqrt[3]{3.6^2 + 91 \times 3.7}}{\sqrt{6.25} + 1.8^3} = 0.845\,537\,207$

**b** $0.845\,537\,207 = 0.846$ to 3 sf

*1 mark for each correct answer.*

**5.** Volume of box $= 8^3 = 512\,\text{cm}^3$

Volume of small cubes $= 2^3 = 8\,\text{cm}^3$

$512 \div 8 = 64$ cubes will fit in the box.

Alternatively, $8 \div 2 = 4$, so 4 cubes fit along each side of the box and the total number of cubes that fit is $4^3 = 64$ cubes.

*1 mark for volume of box (or for finding that 4 cubes fit along each side); 1 mark for volume of small cubes (or for $4^3$); 1 mark for correct answer. Total 3 marks.*

## Page 15, Calculating with indices

**1.** $7^2 \times 7^5 = 7^{2+5} = 7^7$

*1 mark for correct answer circled. When multiplying numbers with the same base, add the powers and keep the base the same.*

**2. a** $9^{10} \div 9^4 = 9^{10-4} = 9^6$    **b** $2^5 \times 2^{-3} = 2^{5+(-3)} = 2^2$

**c** $7^{-2} \div 7^{-6} = 7^{-2-(-6)} = 7^4$    **d** $(3^4)^4 = 3^{4 \times 4} = 3^{16}$

*1 mark for each correct answer.*

**3. a** $(8^2)^{-5} = 8^{2 \times (-5)} = 8^{-10}$

*1 mark for correct answer.*

**b** $\frac{9^3}{9^2 \times 9^4} = \frac{9^3}{9^6} = 9^{3-6} = 9^{-3}$

*1 mark for $9^6$ in the denominator; 1 mark for correct answer.*

**c** $(2^7 \times 2^4)^{-1} = (2^{7+4})^{-1} = (2^{11})^{-1} = 2^{11 \times (-1)} = 2^{-11}$

*1 mark for $2^{11}$ in the bracket; 1 mark for correct answer.*

**4.** Area $= 10^3 \times 10^2 = 10^5\,\text{cm}^2$

*1 mark for multiplying the two lengths; 1 mark for correct answer.*

**5.** Peter has multiplied the bases. Since the bases are different this cannot be simplified as a simple power of 10

*1 mark for a correct explanation.*

**6. a** $13^0 = 1$

*1 mark for correct answer.*

**b** $8^{-1} = \frac{1}{8}$

*1 mark for correct answer.*

**c** $\left(\frac{2}{5}\right)^3 = \frac{2^3}{5^3} = \frac{8}{125}$

*1 mark for correct answer.*

**d** $\left(\frac{1}{4}\right)^{-2} = 4^2 = 16$

*1 mark for 4; 1 mark for correct answer.*

## Page 16, Factors and multiples

**1. a** 3 or 6    **b** 18 or 36    **c** 24 or 36
   **d** 8    **e** 10 and 30    **f** Any two of 3, 6, 10 and 30
*1 mark for each correct answer. Just one correct answer needed to get each mark.*

**2.** Multiples of 9: 9, 18, 27, ⓡ36, 45, …
Multiples of 12: 12, 24, ⓡ36, 48, …
LCM(9, 12) = 36
*1 mark for any correct answer circled.*

**3.** Factors of 18: 1, 2, 3, ⑥, 9, 18
Factors of 12: 1, 2, 3, 4, ⑥, 12
HCF(18, 12) = 6
*1 mark for any correct common factor; 1 mark for correct answer.*

**4.** Multiples of 6: 6, 12, 18, 24, ㉚, 36, …
Multiples of 5: 5, 10, 15, 20, 25, ㉚, 35, …
Multiples of 15: 15, ㉚, 45, …
LCM(6, 5 and 15) = 30
The alarms next beep together after 30 minutes.
*1 mark for any correct common multiple; 1 mark for correct answer.*

**5.** Multiples of 4: 4, 8, ⑫, 16, ⑳, …
Factors of 60: 1, 2, 3, 4, 5, 6, 10, ⑫, 15, ⑳, 30, 60
HCF(12, 20) = 4 and LCM(12, 20) = 60
The two numbers are 12 and 20
*1 mark for writing two numbers with a HCF of 4 or two numbers with a LCM of 60; 1 mark for correct answer.*

## Page 17, Prime factor decomposition

*You might use a factor tree in your working with the same start and end as shown here but with different middle branches.*

**1.**

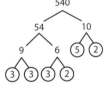

$110 = 2 \times 5 \times 11$
*1 mark for finding or listing the prime factors; 1 mark for correct answer.*

**2. a**

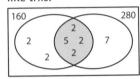

$540 = 2^2 \times 3^3 \times 5$
*1 mark for finding or listing the prime factors; 1 mark for correct answer.*

**b** Since $15 = 3 \times 5$ and both 3 and 5 are prime factors of 540, 540 must be divisible by 15
*1 mark for a correct explanation.*

**3. a**

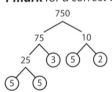

$750 = 2 \times 3 \times 5^3$
*1 mark for finding or listing the prime factors; 1 mark for correct answer.*

**b** Since $4 = 2 \times 2$, but 750 only contains the factor of 2 once, 750 is not divisible by 4
*1 mark for a correct explanation.*

**4. a** $2 \times 3^2 \times 7 \times 13$ is even since 2 is a prime factor.
*1 mark for correct answer.*

**b** To double a number, you multiply by 2, so the prime factor decomposition of a number twice as big will have another factor of 2. This is $2^2 \times 3^2 \times 7 \times 13$
*1 mark for correct answer.*

**5.** The prime factors of each number are:
$4 = 2 \times 2; 5 = 5; 6 = 2 \times 3$
Any number divisible by 4, 5 and 6 must have at least two 2s, one 5 and a 3, so the smallest such number is
$2^2 \times 3 \times 5$
*1 mark for correct answer circled. Note 4 is not prime.*

## Page 18, Finding HCF and LCM

**1. a** $160 = 2^5 \times 5$
*1 mark for correct answer circled.*

**b** $280 = 2^3 \times 5 \times 7$
A Venn diagram showing the prime factors looks like this:

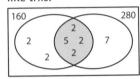

$HCF(160, 280) = 2^3 \times 5 = 40$
*1 mark for multiplying the common factors; 1 mark for correct answer.*

**c** From the Venn diagram,
$LCM(160, 280) = 2 \times 2 \times 2 \times 2 \times 2 \times 5 \times 7 = 1120$
*1 mark for multiplying all the appropriate factors; 1 mark for correct answer.*

**2.**

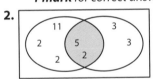

**a** $HCF = 2 \times 5 = 10$
**b** $LCM = 2 \times 2 \times 11 \times 2 \times 5 \times 3 \times 3 = 3960$
*1 mark for correct Venn diagram or alternative method; 1 mark for HCF; 1 mark for LCM. Total 3 marks.*

**3.** $225 = 3^2 \times 5^2$
$324 = 2^2 \times 3^4$
A Venn diagram would look like this:

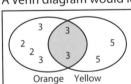

The HCF of the two numbers is 9, so Fran can sort her books into piles of a maximum of 9 if they are to be the same size.
*1 mark for the prime factors of 225; 1 mark for the prime factors of 324; 1 mark for correct answer. Total 3 marks.*

## Page 19, Standard form

**1.** $1.56 \times 10^8 = 156\,000\,000$
*1 mark for correct answer.*

**2.** $8.02 \times 10^{-3} = 0.008\,02$
*1 mark for correct answer circled. Note the negative power of 10 in the question.*

**3. a** $48\,000\,000\,000 = 4.8 \times 10^{10}$   **b** $0.000\,0703 = 7.03 \times 10^{-5}$

**c** $95 \times 10^6 = 9.5 \times 10^7$     **d** $0.68 \times 10^{-4} = 6.8 \times 10^{-5}$
*1 mark for each correct answer.*

4. $150\,000\,000\,km = 1.5 \times 10^8\,km$
*1 mark for correct answer.*

5. Putting all the numbers in either standard or ordinary form:
$2.1 \times 10^4 = 21\,000$, $2.3 \times 10^5 = 230\,000$,
$0.21 \times 10^4 = 2.1 \times 10^3 = 2100$, $2200 = 2.2 \times 10^3$
The order, starting with the biggest, is $2.3 \times 10^5$, $2.1 \times 10^4$, 2200, $0.21 \times 10^4$
*1 mark for converting at least two of the numbers correctly to an alternative form; 1 mark for any three in the correct order; 1 mark for all in the correct order. Total 3 marks.*

6. Virus: $0.000\,000\,05 = 5 \times 10^{-8}\,m$
Bacteria cell: $4 \times 10^{-7} = 0.000\,0004\,m$
The virus is smaller.
*1 mark for getting both numbers in the same form; 1 mark for correct conclusion.*

## Page 20, Calculating with standard form

1. **a** $6 \times 10^2$     **b** $2 \times 10^{-4}$
  **c** $8 \times 10^{-2}$     **d** $6 \times 10^7$
*1 mark for each correct answer.*

2. Everly is not correct. 18 is not between 1 and 10 so it is not in standard form. The correct answer is $1.8 \times 10^7$
*1 mark for 'No' and correct explanation.*

3. $30\,000 = 3 \times 10^4$
$(7 \times 10^{-2}) \times (3 \times 10^4) = 21 \times 10^{(-2)+4} = 21 \times 10^2 = 2.1 \times 10^3$
*1 mark for correct answer circled.*

4. **a** $(5 \times 10^4) + (6 \times 10^5) = 50\,000 + 600\,000 = 650\,000$
$\qquad\qquad = 6.5 \times 10^5$
*1 mark for converting to ordinary numbers or the same power of 10; 1 mark for correct answer.*
  **b** $(9 \times 10^{-3}) - (3 \times 10^{-4}) = 0.009 - 0.0003 = 0.0087$
$\qquad\qquad = 8.7 \times 10^{-3}$
*1 mark for converting to ordinary numbers or the same power of 10; 1 mark for correct answer.*
  **c** $(2.1 \times 10^8) \times (3 \times 10^{-5}) = 6.3 \times 10^{8+(-5)} = 6.3 \times 10^3$
*1 mark for $10^3$; 1 mark for correct answer.*
  **d** $(8.2 \times 10^3) \div (4.1 \times 10^7) = 2 \times 10^{3-7} = 2 \times 10^{-4}$
*1 mark for $10^{-4}$; 1 mark for correct answer.*

## Page 21, Terms and expressions

1. **a** $n - 2$
*1 mark for correct answer circled.*
  **b** $n - 2 + 11 = n + 9$
*1 mark for correct answer.*

2. $3g$
*1 mark for correct answer.*

3. $2x + 3y$
*1 mark for 2x or 3y; 1 mark for correct answer.*

4. $7 + 4p + 3q$
*1 mark for correct answer (the three terms can be written in any order).*

5. **a** $2a + 3b = 2 \times 5 + 3 \times 2 = 10 + 6 = 16$
  **b** $10 - c = 10 - (-4) = 14$
  **c** $\frac{8a}{c} = \frac{8 \times 5}{-4} = \frac{40}{-4} = -10$
  **d** $ac + b = 5 \times (-4) + 2 = -20 + 2 = -18$
*For each part, 1 mark for substituting the numbers in the correct place; 1 mark for correct answer.*

## Page 22, Simplifying expressions

1. **a** $2x + 3x - x = 4x$
*1 mark for correct answer.*
  **b** $3p - 5q + 7q - 2q + 4p = 7p$
*1 mark for 7p or 0q; 1 mark for correct answer.*
  **c** $7 + 5t - 2 - 9t = 5 - 4t$
*1 mark for 5 or −4t; 1 mark for correct answer.*

2. **a** $x^2 + 4x + 3x^2 - 6x + 1 = 4x^2 - 2x + 1$
*1 mark for $4x^2$ or −2x; 1 mark for correct answer.*
  **b** $9mn - 2m^2 + 7nm + 11m^2 = 16mn + 9m^2$
*1 mark for 16mn or $9m^2$; 1 mark for correct answer (terms can be written in any order).*

3. $2x + 3x + x + 2 + x - 1 = 7x + 1$
*1 mark for adding all the sides together; 1 mark for correct answer.*

4.
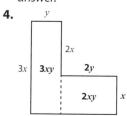

$3xy + 2xy = 5xy$
*1 mark for 3xy; 1 mark for 2xy; 1 mark for correct answer. Total 3 marks.*
*Note that there are alternative methods.*

5. Nikita: $x$, Gabriella: $2x$, Paulo: $x + 2x + 3 = 3x + 3$
Total number of figures: $x + 2x + 3x + 3 = 6x + 3$
*1 mark for 2x; 1 mark for 3x + 3; 1 mark for correct answer. Total 3 marks.*

## Page 23, Formulae

1. **a** Cost $= 80 + 5 \times 15 = 80 + 75 = £155$
*1 mark for substituting in; 1 mark for correct answer.*
  **b** $\frac{275 - 80}{15} = 13$ hours
*1 mark for 195 or subtracting 80 first; 1 mark for correct answer.*

2. **a** $d = \frac{4 + 5}{2} = \frac{9}{2} = 4.5$
*1 mark for substituting in; 1 mark for correct answer.*
  **b** $d = 4^2 - 3 \times 4 = 16 - 12 = 4$
*1 mark for substituting in; 1 mark for correct answer.*
  **c** $\quad 4 = 2d - 12$
$\qquad 2d = 4 + 12 = 16$
$\qquad\; d = \frac{16}{2} = 8$
*1 mark for substituting in; 1 mark for rearranging; 1 mark for correct answer. Total 3 marks.*

3. $a = \frac{24 - 0}{8} = \frac{24}{8} = 3\,m/s^2$
*1 mark for substituting in; 1 mark for correct answer.*

4. $C = 100 + 40t$ or $C = 40t + 100$
*1 mark for 40t + 100; 1 mark for correct answer.*

5. Number of tablets $= \frac{17.5}{3.5} = 5$
*1 mark for substituting in; 1 mark for correct answer.*

## Page 24, Equations and identities

1.

| Expression | Formula | Equation | Identity |
|------------|---------|----------|----------|
| e, g | b, f | (a), c | d, h |

*1 mark for each correct answer. Total 7 marks.*

**2. A, D, E**

*1 mark for each correct answer. Total 3 marks.*

**3.** Seb is wrong since $5x - 2$ cannot be simplified ($5x$ and $-2$ are not like terms). It's only true for $x = 1$, so it's not an identity.

*1 mark for a correct explanation.*

## Page 25, Functions

**1. a** $1 \times 7 + 2 = 9$

   *1 mark for correct answer.*

   **b** $5 \times 7 + 2 = 37$

   *1 mark for correct answer.*

   **c** $-2 \times 7 + 2 = -12$

   *1 mark for correct answer.*

   **d** $(23 - 2) \div 7 = 3$

   *1 mark for attempting to apply inverse operations in correct order; 1 mark for correct answer.*

   **e** $(-26 - 2) \div 7 = -4$

   *1 mark for attempting to apply inverse operations in correct order; 1 mark for correct answer.*

**2. a** $6 \times 3 - 10 = 8$

   *1 mark for correct answer.*

   **b** $1 \times 3 - 10 = -7$

   *1 mark for correct answer.*

   **c** $(2 + 10) \div 3 = 4$

   *1 mark for attempting to apply inverse operations in correct order; 1 mark for correct answer.*

   **d** $y = 3x - 10$

   *1 mark for correct answer.*

**3. a** $(5 - 5) \div 2 + 4 = 4$

   *1 mark for correct answer.*

   **b** $(-1 - 4) \times 2 + 5 = -5$

   *1 mark for attempting to apply inverse operations in correct order; 1 mark for correct answer.*

   **c** $\frac{h - 5}{2} + 4$

   *1 mark for applying first two steps correctly; 1 mark for correct answer.*

## Page 26, Solving linear equations

**1. a** $4t = 28; t = \frac{28}{4} = 7$

   *1 mark for correct answer.*

   **b** $w + 6 = 15; w = 15 - 6 = 9$

   *1 mark for correct answer.*

   **c** $15 - p = 8; p = 15 - 8 = 7$

   *1 mark for correct answer.*

   **d** $\frac{b}{5} = 10; b = 10 \times 5 = 50$

   *1 mark for correct answer.*

**2. a** $2x + 4 = 9; 2x = 9 - 4 = 5; x = \frac{5}{2}$ or 2.5

   *1 mark for $2x = 5$; 1 mark for correct answer.*

   **b** $19 = 3y - 2; 21 = 3y; y = \frac{21}{3} = 7$

   *1 mark for $3y = 21$; 1 mark for correct answer.*

   **c** $-4 = 5q + 6; -10 = 5q; q = -\frac{10}{5} = -2$

   *1 mark for $5q = -10$; 1 mark for correct answer.*

**3. a** $3x + 3x + (x + 1) + (x + 1) = 8x + 2$

   *1 mark for correct answer circled. Remember to include the sides that aren't labelled. Terms 1 and x aren't like terms so the expression cannot be simplified further.*

   **b** $8x + 2 = 38; 8x = 36; x = \frac{36}{8} = \frac{9}{2}$ or 4.5

   *1 mark for writing your expression from part **a** equal to 38; 1 mark for correct answer.*

**4.** Sarah: $n$, Ewan: $n - 5$, Cameron: $2n$

Total: $n + (n - 5) + 2n = 35$
$$4n - 5 = 35$$
$$4n = 40$$
$$n = 10, \text{ so Sarah plays 10 holes.}$$

*1 mark for $n - 5$ and $2n$; 1 mark for adding and writing equal to 35; 1 mark for correct answer. Total 3 marks.*

## Page 27, Harder linear equations

**1. a** $\frac{a}{4} - 1 = 10; \frac{a}{4} = 11; a = 11 \times 4 = 44$

   *1 mark for $\frac{a}{4} = 11$; 1 mark for correct answer.*

   **b** $11 = 2 + \frac{c}{3}; 9 = \frac{c}{3}; c = 9 \times 3 = 27$

   *1 mark for $\frac{c}{3} = 9$; 1 mark for correct answer.*

   **c** $\frac{f - 5}{4} = 10; f - 5 = 40; f = 45$

   *1 mark for $f - 5 = 40$; 1 mark for correct answer.*

**2. a** $\frac{2k + 1}{3} = -4; 2k + 1 = -12; 2k = -13; k = -\frac{13}{2} = -6.5$

   *1 mark for $2k + 1 = -12$; 1 mark for correct answer.*

   **b** $5p + 3 = 3p + 7; 5p - 3p = 7 - 3; 2p = 4; p = 2$

   *1 mark for $2p = 4$; 1 mark for correct answer.*

   **c** $3 + p = 4p - 6; 3 + 6 = 4p - p; 9 = 3p; p = 3$

   *1 mark for $9 = 3p$; 1 mark for correct answer.*

   **d** $9 - 6p = 4 - 11p; -6p + 11p = 4 - 9; 5p = -5;$
   $p = \frac{-5}{5} = -1$

   *1 mark for $5p = -5$; 1 mark for correct answer.*

**3.** $2x + 3 = 3x - 4; 3 + 4 = 3x - 2x; 7 = x; x = 7$

Rosalind's number is 7

*1 mark for correct equation; 1 mark for correct rearrangement; 1 mark for correct answer. Total 3 marks.*

**4. a** $2x - 1 = x + 3; 2x - x = 3 + 1; x = 4$

   *1 mark for correct equation; 1 mark for correct rearrangement; 1 mark for correct answer. Total 3 marks.*

   **b** If $x = 4$, the shorter side is $x + 3 = 4 + 3 = 7$ cm
   (or $2x - 1 = 2 \times 4 - 1 = 7$ cm).
   The perimeter is $7 + 7 + y + y = 14 + 2y$
   $14 + 2y = 34; 2y = 20; y = 10$
   This means the area of the rectangle is $10 \times 7 = 70 \text{ cm}^2$.

   *1 mark for finding the length of the shorter side (7 cm); 1 mark for setting up an equation to find y; 1 mark for y = 10; 1 mark for correct answer. Total 4 marks.*

## Page 28, Rearranging formulae

**1. a** $q = p + 3r; q - 3r = p; p = q - 3r$

   *1 mark for correct answer.*

   **b** $r = 3p + 2; r - 2 = 3p; p = \frac{r - 2}{3}$

   *1 mark for making 3p the subject; 1 mark for correct answer.*

   **c** $q = p^2; p = \pm\sqrt{q}$

   *1 mark for correct answer (± sign not needed for mark).*

   **d** $\frac{q + p}{6} = r; q + p = 6r; p = 6r - q$

   *1 mark for making 6r the subject; 1 mark for correct answer.*

**2. a** $2x^2 - 3 = y; 2x^2 = y + 3; x^2 = \frac{y + 3}{2}; x = \pm\sqrt{\frac{y + 3}{2}}$

   *1 mark for making $x^2$ the subject; 1 mark for correct answer (± sign not needed for mark). Total 3 marks.*

   **b** $a\sqrt{x} + b = c; a\sqrt{x} = c - b; \sqrt{x} = \frac{c - b}{a}; x = \left(\frac{c - b}{a}\right)^2$

   *1 mark for making $\sqrt{x}$ the subject; 1 mark for correct answer.*

**3.** $p = I^2 R; \frac{p}{R} = I^2; I = \sqrt{\frac{p}{R}}$

    **1 mark** *for making $I^2$ the subject;* **1 mark** *for correct answer.*

**4.** Fleur has made a mistake on line 3 (there should be no square root as $x$ is not squared). It should be:

$x = \frac{y + b}{a^2}$

    **1 mark** *for identifying mistake on line 3;* **1 mark** *for correct working or correct explanation.*

## Page 29, Expanding single brackets

**1. a** $5(x + 3) = 5x + 15$

    **1 mark** *for correct answer.*

  **b** $a(x - 2) = ax - 2a$

    **1 mark** *for $ax$;* **1 mark** *for $-2a$.*

  **c** $2x(3x - y) = 6x^2 - 2xy$

    **1 mark** *for $6x^2$;* **1 mark** *for $-2xy$.*

  **d** $(5x - 1)x = 5x^2 - x$

    **1 mark** *for $5x^2$; 1 for $-x$.*

**2. a** $2(x + 4) + 3(x - 8) = 2x + 8 + 3x - 24 = 5x - 16$

  **b** $9(x + 2) - 4(2x - 1) = 9x + 18 - 8x + 4 = x + 22$

  **c** $4(y + 3) - (y + 2) = 4y + 12 - y - 2 = 3y + 10$

  *For each part,* **1 mark** *for expanding the first bracket correctly;* **1 mark** *for expanding the second bracket correctly;* **1 mark** *for the correct answer. Total 3 marks.*

**3.** Area $= \frac{1}{2} \times (2x + 8) \times 3z = (x + 4) \times 3z = 3xz + 12z$

    **1 mark** *for $\frac{1}{2} \times (2x + 8) \times 3z$ (written in any order);* **1 mark** *for $3xz$;* **1 mark** *for $12z$. Total 3 marks.*

**4.** Area of square $= 3x \times 3x = 9x^2$

    Area of rectangle $= 2x(x - 4) = 2x^2 - 8x$

    Difference between areas $= 9x^2 - (2x^2 - 8x) = 7x^2 + 8x$

    **1 mark** *for area of square;* **1 mark** *for area of rectangle;* **1 mark** *for getting to correct difference. Total 3 marks.*

## Page 30, Factorising into single brackets

**1. a** $2(2x + 3y)$      **b** $5(2x - y)$      **c** $p(q - 2)$

    **1 mark** *for each correct answer.*

**2.** $12a + 30b = 6(2a + 5b)$

    **1 mark** *for correct answer circled.*

**3. a** $5x(4x - 1)$      **b** $2p(4q - 3p)$

  **c** $5y(z - 4)$      **d** $4x(4 + 3y)$

  **e** $xy(x + y)$      **f** $2p(4 - 2pq + 3q)$

  *For each part,* **1 mark** *for removing any common factor;* **1 mark** *for fully factorising correctly.*

**4.** $x^2 + 3x = x(x + 3)$, so the length is $x + 3$

    **1 mark** *for correct answer.*

**5.** $4xz + 10xyz = 2xz(2 + 5y)$ if factorised fully.

    This gives width and length of $2xz$ and $2 + 5y$. There are alternative answers if you don't factorise fully e.g. $x$ and $4z + 10yz$, $2x$ and $2z + 5yz$, $z$ and $4x + 10xy$, etc.

    **1 mark** *for a correct factorisation;* **1 mark** *for writing the length and width from this factorisation.*

## Page 31, Expanding double brackets

**1. a** $x^2 + 7x + 5x + 35 = x^2 + 12x + 35$

  **b** $m^2 - 3m + 4m - 12 = m^2 + m - 12$

  **c** $y^2 - 5y - 4y + 20 = y^2 - 9y + 20$

  **d** $(x + 3)(x + 3) = x^2 + 3x + 3x + 9 = x^2 + 6x + 9$

  *For each part,* **1 mark** *for a correct expansion without simplifying;* **1 mark** *for a correct simplified expansion (terms written in any order).*

**2.** $(y - 8)^2 = y^2 - 8y - 8y + 64 = y^2 - 16y + 64$

    **1 mark** *for correct answer circled.*

**3. a** $xy + x + 2y + 2$

  **b** $4a - 10 + 2a^2 - 5a = 2a^2 - a - 10$

  **c** $(a + b)(a + b) = a^2 + ab + ba + b^2 = a^2 + 2ab + b^2$

  **d** $6m^2 - 4mn + 9nm - 6n^2 = 6m^2 + 5mn - 6n^2$

  **e** $(4x + 1)(4x + 1) = 16x^2 + 4x + 4x + 1 = 16x^2 + 8x + 1$

  *For each part,* **1 mark** *for a correct expansion without simplifying;* **1 mark** *for a correct simplified expansion (terms written in any order).*

**4.** Area $= \frac{1}{2} \times$ base $\times$ height $= \frac{1}{2} \times (2x + 2) \times (2x - 1)$

    $\frac{1}{2}$ the base is $x + 1$, so this becomes:

    $(x + 1)(2x - 1) = 2x^2 + 2x - x - 1 = 2x^2 + x - 1$

    **1 mark** *for writing $\frac{1}{2} \times$ base $\times$ height and putting the expressions $2x + 2$ and $2x - 1$ into this formula;* **1 mark** *for expanding the brackets correctly (unsimplified);* **1 mark** *for the correct answer. Total 3 marks.*

## Page 32, Factorising into double brackets

*Note that, when factorising, brackets can be written in any order.*

**1. a** $(x + 2)(x + 3)$      **b** $(y - 2)(y - 1)$

  **c** $(p - 12)(p + 3)$      **d** $(x + 10)(x - 1)$

  **e** $(y - 7)(y - 7) = (y - 7)^2$      **f** $(x + 4)(x + 4) = (x + 4)^2$

  *For each part,* **1 mark** *for double brackets including two numbers that multiply to give the constant term;* **1 mark** *for correct answer.*

**2.** $x^2 + 6x - 27 = (x + 9)(x - 3)$, so the sides of the rectangle are $x + 9$ and $x - 3$

    **1 mark** *for factorising correctly;* **1 mark** *for giving the two sides.*

**3.** Pavel is wrong because he needs two numbers with a sum of 5 but a product of $-6$, not 6. (These numbers are 6 and $-1$, so $x^2 + 5x - 6 = (x + 6)(x - 1)$.)

    **1 mark** *for an expression that either factorises correctly or an explanation that notes that the product of the two numbers must be $-6$, not 6*

**4.** $x^2 + 6x + 9 = (x + 3)^2 = (x + 3)(x + 3)$

    The side length of the square is $x + 3$

    Perimeter $= 4(x + 3) = 4x + 12$

    **1 mark** *for factorising correctly;* **1 mark** *for summing up four lots of $x + 3$ or for multiplying $x + 3$ by 4;* **1 mark** *for the correct answer. Total 3 marks.*

## Page 33, Difference of two squares

*Note that, when factorising, brackets can be written in any order.*

**1. a** $x^2 - 2x + 2x - 4 = x^2 - 4$

  **b** $y^2 + 10y - 10y - 100 = y^2 - 100$

  **c** $p^2 - 3p + 3p - 9 = p^2 - 9$

  *For each part,* **1 mark** *for a correct unsimplified expansion;* **1 mark** *for the correct simplified expansion.*

**2. a** $(x - 7)(x + 7)$      **b** $(y - 9)(y + 9)$

  **c** $(b - 11)(b + 11)$      **d** $(p - 3q)(p + 3q)$

    **1 mark** *for each correct answer.*

**3. a** $y(y + 16)$

    **1 mark** *for correct answer.*

  **b** $(x - 4)(x + 4)$

    **1 mark** *for correct answer.*

**c** $(a + 8)(a + 8) = (a + 8)^2$

   *1 mark for brackets with a and two numbers that multiply to give 64; 1 mark for the correct answer.*

**d** $(q - 10)(q - 6)$

   *1 mark for brackets with q and two numbers that multiply to give 60; 1 mark for the correct answer.*

**e** $(n - 12)(n + 12)$

   *1 mark for correct answer.*

**4.** The area of a parallelogram is given by base × height. Since $x^2 - 121 = (x + 11)(x - 11)$, the base and height are $x + 11$ and $x - 11$

   *1 mark for factorising the area; 1 mark for writing down the base and height.*

## Page 34, Solving quadratic equations

**1. a** $(x + 4)(x + 5) = 0$
   $x = -4$ or $x = -5$

**b** $(x - 8)(x + 1) = 0$
   $x = 8$ or $x = -1$

**c** $x(x + 5) = 0$
   $x = 0$ or $x = -5$

**d** $(x - 1)(x + 1) = 0$
   $x = 1$ or $x = -1$

   *For each part, 1 mark for factorising; 1 mark for correct answer from your factorisation; 1 mark for both correct answers. Total 3 marks.*

**2. a** $2x(x + 3) = 0$
   $x = 0$ or $x = -3$

   *1 mark for factorising; 1 mark for 0; 1 mark for -3. Total 3 marks.*

**b** $x^2 - 12x + 35 = 0$
   $(x - 7)(x - 5) = 0$
   $x = 7$ or $x = 5$

   *1 mark for rearranging to equal 0; 1 mark for factorising; 1 mark for 7; 1 mark for 5. Total 4 marks.*

**c** $x^2 + 3x - 10 = 0$
   $(x + 5)(x - 2) = 0$
   $x = -5$ or $x = 2$

   *1 mark for rearranging to equal 0; 1 mark for factorising; 1 mark for -5; 1 mark for 2. Total 4 marks.*

**d** $x^2 - 144 = 0$
   $(x - 12)(x + 12) = 0$
   $x = 12$ or $x = -12$

   *1 mark for rearranging and factorising or for 12 from taking square root; 1 mark for -12*

**3. a** Length × width is $(x - 4)(x - 5)$
   Since the area is 12 cm², you have $(x - 4)(x - 5) = 12$
   $x^2 - 4x - 5x + 20 = 12$
   $x^2 - 9x + 20 = 12$
   $x^2 - 9x + 8 = 0$

   *1 mark for $(x - 4)(x - 5) = 12$; 1 mark for expanding and trying to rearrange to make 0; 1 mark for correct working to reach the final answer. Total 3 marks.*

**b** $x^2 - 9x + 8 = 0$
   $(x - 8)(x - 1) = 0$
   $x = 8$ or $x = 1$
   If $x = 1$, then $x - 4 = -3$ and $x - 5 = -4$, which gives negative side lengths. This is impossible, so you must use $x = 8$, giving $x - 4 = 4$ and $x - 5 = 3$, so the shortest side length is 3 cm.

   *1 mark for factorising; 1 mark for the solutions 8 and 1; 1 mark for the correct answer. Total 3 marks.*

## Page 35, Simultaneous equations 1

**1. a** $x + y = 14$ (1), $x - y = 8$ (2)
   (1) + (2): $2x = 22$; $x = 11$
   Substituting into (1): $11 + y = 14$; $y = 3$

   *1 mark for adding or subtracting the equations to eliminate either x or y; 1 mark for x = 11 and y = 3*

**b** $2x - 2y = 4$ (1), $2x + 3y = 14$ (2)
   (1) − (2): $-5y = -10$; $y = 2$
   Substituting into (1): $2x - 4 = 4$; $2x = 8$, $x = 4$

   *1 mark for subtracting the equations to eliminate y; 1 mark for x = 4; 1 mark for y = 2. Total 3 marks.*

**c** $4x + 5y = 37$ (1), $2x + y = 11$ (2)
   (2) × 2: $4x + 2y = 22$
   (1) − (2) × 2: $3y = 15$; $y = 5$
   Substituting into (2): $2x + 5 = 11$; $2x = 6$; $x = 3$

   *1 mark for correct equation in either x or y; 1 mark for x = 3; 1 mark for y = 5. Total 3 marks.*

**d** $3x - 2y = 2$ (1), $12x - 4y = 10$ (2)
   (1) × 4: $12x - 8y = 8$ (3)
   (3) − (2): $-4y = -2$; $y = \frac{1}{2}$ or 0.5
   Substituting into (1): $3x - 1 = 2$; $3x = 3$; $x = 1$

   *1 mark for correct equation in either x or y; 1 mark for x = 1; 1 mark for y = 0.5. Total 3 marks.*

**2. a** $2x + 5y = 11$ (1), $3x - 2y = -12$ (2)
   (1) × 2: $4x + 10y = 22$ (3)
   (2) × 5: $15x - 10y = -60$ (4)
   (3) + (4): $19x = -38$; $x = -2$
   Substituting into (1): $-4 + 5y = 11$; $5y = 15$; $y = 3$

**b** $2x - 7y = 12$ (1), $5x - y = -3$ (2)
   (2) × 7: $35x - 7y = -21$ (3)
   (1) − (3): $-33x = 33$; $x = -1$
   Substitute into (2): $-5 - y = -3$; $y = -2$

**c** $3x + 8y = 12$ (1), $2x + 12y = 13$ (2)
   (1) × 2: $6x + 16y = 24$ (3)
   (2) × 3: $6x + 36y = 39$ (4)
   (3) − (4): $-20y = -15$; $y = \frac{15}{20} = \frac{3}{4}$ or 0.75
   Substituting into (1): $3x + 6 = 12$; $3x = 6$; $x = 2$

**d** $6x - 4y = 9$ (1), $5x + 3y = -2$ (2)
   (1) × 3: $18x - 12y = 27$ (3)
   (2) × 4: $20x + 12y = -8$ (4)
   (3) + (4): $38x = 19$; $x = \frac{1}{2}$ or 0.5
   Substituting into (1):
   $3 - 4y = 9$; $4y = -6$; $y = -\frac{6}{4} = -\frac{3}{2}$ or −1.5

   *For each part, 1 mark for correct equation in either x or y; 1 mark for x solution; 1 mark for y solution. Total 3 marks.*

## Page 36, Simultaneous equations 2

**1. a** Let $a$ be the price of an adult ticket and $c$ the price of a child ticket.
   $a + 3c = 39$ (1), $2a + 4c = 62$ (2)

   *1 mark for the first equation (any letters for your variables score); 1 mark for the second equation.*

**b** (1) × 2: $2a + 6c = 78$ (3)
   (3) − (2): $2c = 16$; $c = 8$
   Substitute into (1): $a + 24 = 39$, $a = 15$
   An adult ticket costs £15 and a child ticket costs £8.

   *1 mark for correct equation in either a or c; 1 mark for adult ticket is £15; 1 mark for child ticket is £8. Total 3 marks.*

**2.** Let $a$ be the mass of an apple and $s$ be the mass of a satsuma.

$20a + 30s = 4050$ (1), $12a + 15s = 2205$ (2)

(2) × 2: $24a + 30s = 4410$ (3)

(1) – (3): $-4a = -360$; $a = 90$

Substituting into (2):

$1080 + 15s = 2205$; $15s = 1125$; $s = 75$

The mass of an apple is 90 g and the mass of a satsuma is 75 g.

***1 mark** for correct simultaneous equations; **1 mark** for correct equation in either a or s; **1 mark** for apple mass of 90 g; **1 mark** for satsuma mass of 75 g. Total 4 marks.*

**3.** $6x + y = 108$ (1), $4x + 2y = 128$ (2)

(1) × 2: $12x + 2y = 216$ (3)

(3) – (2): $8x = 88$; $x = 11$

Substituting into (1): $66 + y = 108$; $y = 42$

The area of a square is 11 cm² and the area of a rectangle is 42 cm².

***1 mark** for correct simultaneous equations; **1 mark** for correct equation in either x or y; **1 mark** for square area 11 cm²; **1 mark** for rectangle area 42 cm². Total 4 marks.*

## Page 37, Solving inequalities

**1. a**

*1 mark for the correct answer.*

**b**

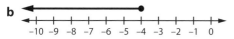

*1 mark for the correct answer.*

**c**

*1 mark for any circles at –2 and 5, joined together; 1 mark for the correct circles.*

**d**

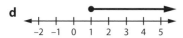

*1 mark for the correct answer.*

**2.** –1, 0, 1, 2, 3, 4

*1 mark for the correct answer.*

**3.** $-3 < n \leq 4$, so $n$ could be –2, –1, 0, 1, 2, 3, 4

*1 mark for dividing –6 and 8 by 2; 1 mark for the correct answer.*

**4. a** $x \geq 2.5$

*1 mark for 2.5; 1 mark for $x \geq 2.5$*

**b** $2x < 6$; $x < 3$

*1 mark for $2x < 6$ or $2x = 6$; 1 mark for 3; 1 mark for $x < 3$. Total 3 marks.*

**c** $3x > -3$; $x > -1$

*1 mark for $3x > -3$ or $3x = -3$; 1 mark for –1; 1 mark for $x > -1$. Total 3 marks.*

**d** $20 \geq 5x$; $4 \geq x$; $x \leq 4$

*1 mark for $20 \geq 5x$ or $20 = 5x$; 1 mark for 4; 1 mark for $4 \geq x$ or $x \leq 4$. Total 3 marks.*

## Page 38, Drawing linear graphs

**1. a**

| $x$ | –1 | 0 | 1 | 2 | 3 |
|---|---|---|---|---|---|
| $y$ | –4 | –1 | 2 | 5 | 8 |

*1 mark for two correct values; 1 mark for all three correct.*

**b**

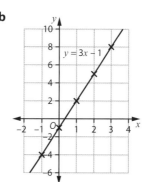

*1 mark for at least three points plotted correctly; 1 mark for a correct graph (straight line drawn through the correct points).*

**2. a**

| $x$ | –2 | –1 | 0 | 1 | 2 |
|---|---|---|---|---|---|
| $y$ | 7 | 6 | 5 | 4 | 3 |

*1 mark for two correct values; 1 mark for all three correct.*

**b**

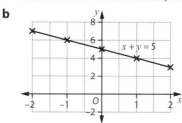

*1 mark for at least three points plotted correctly; 1 mark for a correct graph (straight line drawn through the correct points).*

**3.** Create a table of values, perhaps like this:

| $x$ | –2 | –1 | 0 | 1 | 2 |
|---|---|---|---|---|---|
| $y$ | 7 | 5 | 3 | 1 | –1 |

Next, draw the graph:

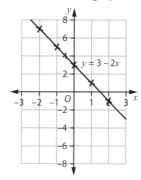

*1 mark for a correct table of values with at least three points (or correct points shown in graph); 1 mark for the points plotted correctly; 1 mark for a correct graph (straight line drawn through the correct points). Total 3 marks.*

## Page 39, Working out gradients

**1. a** Gradient $= \frac{6}{3} = 2$     **b** Gradient $= \frac{2}{4} = \frac{1}{2}$ or 0.5

**c** Gradient $= \frac{-3}{3} = -1$     **d** Gradient $= \frac{-6}{4} = \frac{-3}{2}$ or –1.5

*For each part, **1 mark** for using $\frac{change\ in\ y}{change\ in\ x}$ with any correct values; **1 mark** for correct answer.*

**2. a** Gradient $= \frac{1}{1} = 1$

*1 mark for using $\frac{change\ in\ y}{change\ in\ x}$ with any correct values; 1 mark for correct answer.*

**b** $y = x$

*1 mark for correct answer.*

**3. a** Gradient $= \frac{-6}{2} = -3$

*1 mark for using $\frac{change\ in\ y}{change\ in\ x}$ with any correct values;*
*1 mark for correct answer.*

**b** $y = -3x$

*1 mark for correct answer.*

## Page 40, Equation of a straight line

**1. a** Gradient = 5, $y$-intercept = 1

*1 mark for gradient; 1 mark for $y$-intercept.*

**b** Gradient = −2, $y$-intercept = 3

*1 mark for gradient; 1 mark for $y$-intercept.*

**c** $y = \frac{1}{2}x + 3$
Gradient $= \frac{1}{2}$, $y$-intercept = 3

*1 mark for correctly rearranging; 1 mark for gradient;*
*1 mark for $y$-intercept. Total 3 marks.*

**d** $y = x + 10$
Gradient = 1, $y$-intercept = 10

*1 mark for correctly rearranging; 1 mark for gradient;*
*1 mark for $y$-intercept. Total 3 marks.*

**e** $4y = 3 - 8x$; $y = \frac{3}{4} - 2x$
Gradient = −2, $y$-intercept $= \frac{3}{4}$

*1 mark for correctly rearranging; 1 mark for gradient;*
*1 mark for $y$-intercept. Total 3 marks.*

**2.** A parallel line will also have gradient 4, so $y = 4x + 3$ is correct.

*1 mark for correct answer circled.*

**3. a** Gradient $= \frac{change\ in\ y}{change\ in\ x} = \frac{3 - (-1)}{2 - 0} = \frac{4}{2} = 2$

Equation is $y = 2x + c$
Since the line goes through $(0, -1)$, the $y$-intercept is −1
Equation is $y = 2x - 1$

**b** Gradient $= \frac{change\ in\ y}{change\ in\ x} = \frac{5 - 1}{-3 - 1} = \frac{4}{-4} = -1$

Equation is $y = -x + c$
Substitute one of the coordinates in for $x$ and $y$ to get
e.g. $1 = -1 + c$, giving $c = 2$
Equation is $y = -x + 2$ or $y = 2 - x$

*For each part, 1 mark for the gradient; 1 mark for the*
*$y$-intercept; 1 mark for the correct answer. Total 3 marks.*

**4.** $y = 4 - 3x$ has gradient −3
$3x + y = 0$ rearranges to $y = -3x$
This also has gradient −3, so Sajid is correct.

*1 mark for rearranging and identifying a gradient of −3;*
*1 mark for 'Yes' with a correct explanation.*

## Page 41, Kinematic graphs

**1. a** 30 km

*1 mark for the correct answer.*

**b** Kai's speed is slower because the gradient of the graph is less steep after 12:00

*1 mark for the correct answer.*

**c** Kai travels $30 - 25 = 5$ km in 30 minutes. This would mean 10 km in 1 hour, so his speed is 10 km/h.

*1 mark for finding out how far he would travel in 1 hour;*
*1 mark for the correct answer.*
*Alternatively, 1 mark for working out speed $= \frac{distance}{time}$;*
*1 mark for the correct answer.*

**d** The sections marked '1' and '2' on the graph show the answer.

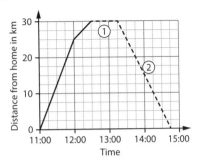

*1 mark for the first horizontal section correct; 1 mark for the second section correct.*

**2. a** 54–55.5 minutes

*1 mark for the correct answer.*

**b** After 9–10.5 minutes

*1 mark for correct answer.*

**c** Krystyna accelerates at a steady rate for 15 minutes until she reaches 12 km/h. She then runs at a steady pace for 30 minutes. For the last 10 minutes she runs at a steady pace of 15 km/h.

*1 mark for describing the first section (using acceleration and mentioning the time and speed); 1 mark for second section (constant speed); 1 mark for third section (constant speed of 15 km/h). Total 3 marks.*

## Page 42, Quadratic graphs

**1. a**

| $x$ | −2 | −1 | 0 | 1 | 2 | 3 |
|---|---|---|---|---|---|---|
| $y$ | 5 | 1 | −1 | −1 | 1 | 5 |

*1 mark for any two answers correct; 1 mark for all four correct.*

**b**

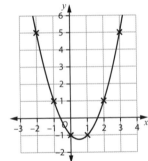

*1 mark for plotting all the points correctly; 1 mark for a smooth curve drawn through the points.*

**c** $(0.5, -1.25)$

*1 mark for an answer close to $(0.5, -1.25)$.*

**2. a** Approximately 1.4 and −1.4

*1 mark for 1.4 (or close); 1 mark for −1.4 (or close).*

**b** $(0, 2)$

*1 mark for correct answer.*

**c** Draw a horizontal line through −3 on the $y$-axis. This line cuts the graph when $x \approx -2.2$ and $x \approx 2.2$

*1 mark for identifying the points where $y = -3$; 1 mark for correct answer (both solutions).*

## Page 43, Solutions from graphs

**1.** The point of intersection is approximately $(2.3, 1.7)$, so $x = 2.3$ and $y = 1.7$

*1 mark for $x$ is (close to) 2.3; 1 mark for $y$ is (close to) 1.7*

**2.** The line to draw is $y = x$. The two lines intersect at (2, 2), so $x = 2$ and $y = 2$

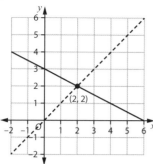

*1 mark for the line $y = x$ drawn; 1 mark for correct answer.*

## Page 44, Cubic and reciprocal graphs

**1.** Top to bottom in table: C, D, A, B
*1 mark for only one correct; 1 mark for two correct; 1 mark for all four correct. Total 3 marks.*

**2. a**

| $x$ | −2 | −1 | 0 | 1 | 2 |
|---|---|---|---|---|---|
| $y$ | **−9** | −2 | −1 | **0** | 7 |

*1 mark for two answers correct; 1 mark for all three correct.*

**b**

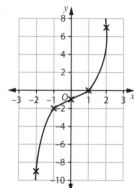

*1 mark for the points plotted correctly; 1 mark for a smooth curve through the points.*

**3. a**

| $x$ | −2 | −1 | 0 | 1 | 2 |
|---|---|---|---|---|---|
| $y$ | −15 | **−1** | **1** | **3** | 17 |

**b**

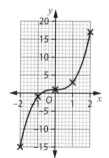

*1 mark for the points plotted correctly; 1 mark for a smooth curve through the points.*

**c** The root is approximately −0.8
*1 mark for −0.8 (or close).*

## Page 45, Rates of change

**1. a** 3, 5, 7 and 9 (The height suddenly goes down.)
*1 mark for correct answer.*

**b** 9–12 (The gradient is the least steep here.)
*1 mark for correct answer.*

**c** It grows 2 cm in 2 weeks, so $\frac{2}{2} = 1$ cm/week.
*1 mark for correct answer.*

**2.** Left to right in table: B, A, C
*1 mark for only one correct; 1 mark for all three correct.*

## Page 46, Sequences

**1.**

| | Sequence | Term-to-term rule | Next term | Seventh term | Type of sequence |
|---|---|---|---|---|---|
| a) | 25, 31, 37, 43 | Add 6 | 49 | 61 | Arithmetic |
| b) | 1, 2, 4, 8 | Multiply by 2 | 16 | 64 | Geometric |
| c) | 20, 10, 5, 2.5 | Divide by 2 | 1.25 | 0.3125 | Geometric |
| d) | 20, 17, 14, 11 | Subtract 3 | 8 | 2 | Arithmetic |

*1 mark for each correct answer. Total 16 marks.*

**2. a** Nick is correct because all the numbers in the sequence end in 2 or 7, and 3075 does not.
*1 mark for correct answer.*

**b** The sequence continues from 27 with 32, 37, 42, 47, 52, 57, so the tenth term is 57
*1 mark for continuing the sequence to at least the tenth term; 1 mark for correct answer.*

**3. a** The sequence starts 3, 5, 7, so Pattern 4 contains 9 dots, and Pattern 5 contains 11 dots.
*1 mark for correct answer.*

**b** Add 2
*1 mark for correct answer.*

**c** It is not possible as all the terms in the sequence are odd numbers and 20 is an even number.
*1 mark for correct answer (including the explanation).*

**4.** Since the sequence is arithmetic, and two consecutive terms are 9 and 15, the term-to-term rule is 'add 6'. This means $a = 9 − 6 = 3$ and $b = 15 + 6 = 21$
*1 mark for $a = 3$; 1 mark for $b = 21$*

## Page 47, Using the nth term

**1.**

| | $n$th term | First four terms | Term-to-term rule | Seventh term | Hundredth term |
|---|---|---|---|---|---|
| a) | $3n − 1$ | 2, 5, 8, 11 | Add 3 | 20 | 299 |
| b) | $5n + 2$ | 7, 12, 17, 22 | Add 5 | 37 | 502 |
| c) | $6 − n$ | 5, 4, 3, 2 | Subtract 1 | −1 | −94 |
| d) | $10 − 3n$ | 7, 4, 1, −2 | Subtract 3 | −11 | −290 |

*1 mark for each correct answer. Total 16 marks.*

**2. a** 6, 9, 14, 21    **b** −1, 0, 3, 8    **c** 9, 6, 1, −6
*For each part, 1 mark for two terms correct; 1 mark for a complete correct answer.*

**3. a** $8n + 3 = 51$; $8n = 48$; $n = \frac{48}{8} = 6$
The 6th term is 51
*1 mark for writing the equation; 1 mark for correct answer.*

**b** $8n + 3 = 64$; $8n = 61$
61 is not divisible by 8, so 64 is not in the sequence.
*1 mark for writing the equation; 1 mark for correct answer.*

**c** $8n + 3 > 100$; $8n > 97$; $n > \frac{97}{8}$ (= 12.125)
This is the 13th term. The 13th term is $8 \times 13 + 3 = 107$
*1 mark for writing the inequality; 1 mark for the 13th term; 1 mark for correct answer. Total 3 marks.*

**4. a** When $n = 4$, $n^2 − 30 = 4^2 − 30 = 16 − 30 = −14$
*1 mark for substituting in 4; 1 mark for correct answer.*

**b** $n^2 - 30 = 114$, so $n^2 = 144$. Since 144 is a square number, $n = 12$ and so 114 is indeed in the sequence.
*1 mark for the equation; 1 mark for correct answer.*

## Page 48, Working out the nth term

**1.**

| | Sequence | Term-to-term rule | $n$th term | Tenth term |
|---|---|---|---|---|
| a) | 17, 23, 29, 35 | Add 6 | $6n + 11$ | 79 |
| b) | −1, 2, 5, 8 | Add 3 | $3n - 4$ | 26 |
| c) | 4, 1, −2, −5 | Subtract 3 | $-3n + 7$ or $7 - 3n$ | −23 |
| d) | 20, 15, 10, 5 | Subtract 5 | $-5n + 25$ or $25 - 5n$ | −25 |
| e) | 3, 3.5, 4, 4.5 | Add 0.5 | $0.5n + 2.5$ | 7.5 |

*1 mark for each correct answer. Total 15 marks.*

**2. a** The sequence goes 3, 7, 11. The term-to-term rule is 'add 4'. The $n$th term is $4n - 1$ as the sequence is 1 less than the four times table.
*1 mark for identifying the sequence; 1 mark for correct answer.*
**b** $4 \times 40 - 1 = 159$
*1 mark for substituting in 40; 1 mark for correct answer.*

**3.** Emilia has confused the term-to-term rule (add 5) with the $n$th term rule. Isabella is correct.
*1 mark for a correct explanation that Isabella is correct.*

**4.** The sequence goes 5, __, 11, …
Since it is arithmetic, it increases by the same amount each time. In two jumps, it increases by 6, so the term-to-term rule is 'add 3' and the sequence is 5, 8, 11, …
This makes the $n$th term $3n + 2$
*1 mark for identifying the sequence; 1 mark for the nth term.*

## Page 49, Special sequences

**1. a** The square numbers
   **b** The Fibonacci sequence
   **c** The cube numbers
   *1 mark for each correct answer.*

**2. a** 16
   **b** $n^2$
   *1 mark for each correct answer.*

**3. a** Each term is the sum of the previous two, so it continues 26 (10 + 16), then 42 (16 + 26) and then 68 (26 + 42). The 8th term is 68
   *1 mark for continuing the sequence for one more term; 1 mark for correct answer.*
   **b i** The next two terms are $5x$ $(2x + 3x)$ and $8x$ $(3x + 5x)$.
   *1 mark for 5x; 1 mark for 8x.*
   **ii** $8x = 32; x = \frac{32}{8} = 4$
   The first term is 4
   *1 mark for the equation; 1 mark for correct answer.*

## Page 50, Proportion

**1.** $\frac{32}{40} \times 100\% = 80\%$
*1 mark for $\frac{32}{40} \times 100\%$; 1 mark for correct answer.*

**2.** $\frac{105}{135} = \frac{7}{9}$
*1 mark for $\frac{105}{135}$; 1 mark for correct answer.*

**3.** $\frac{7000 \times 100\%}{5000} = 140\%$
*1 mark for correct answer circled.*

**4.** $\frac{21}{30} = \frac{7}{10} = \frac{70}{100} = 70\%$
$\frac{18}{25} = \frac{72}{100} = 72\%$
Jazmine is wrong. Her trigonometry score is better.
*1 mark for 70%; 1 mark for 72%; 1 mark for correct answer (e.g. 'Jazmine is wrong' supported by correct working). Total 3 marks.*

**5.** $1\frac{3}{4}$ hours = 105 minutes
0.25 hours = 15 minutes
105 + 15 + 10 = 130 minutes
$\frac{105}{130} = \frac{21}{26}$
*1 mark for either 105 or 15; 1 mark for adding your times and writing as a fraction over 130; 1 mark for correct answer of $\frac{21}{26}$. Total 3 marks.*

**6.** $1 - \frac{2}{3} = \frac{1}{3}$ are children.
$1 - \frac{1}{4} = \frac{3}{4}$, so $\frac{3}{4}$ of the children don't wear glasses.
$\frac{1}{3} \times \frac{3}{4} = \frac{1}{4}$
$\frac{1}{4}$ of the audience are children who don't wear glasses.
*1 mark for $1 - \frac{2}{3} \left(= \frac{1}{3}\right)$; 1 mark for $1 - \frac{1}{4} \left(= \frac{3}{4}\right)$; 1 mark for correct answer of $\frac{1}{4}$ (or equivalent e.g. $\frac{3}{12}$, 25%). Total 3 marks.*

## Page 51, Ratio

**1.** 3 : 7
*1 mark for correct answer circled. The others are not in simplest form or are in wrong order.*

**2.** $\frac{4}{7}$
*1 mark for correct answer.*

**3.** For every two students who walk to school, there is one student who doesn't walk to school.
So, doesn't walk : walk = 1 : 2
*1 mark for 1 : 2*

**4.** Fruit scones : sultanas = 10 : 75 = 2 : 15 = 12 : 90
Noah needs 90 grams of sultanas.
*1 mark for method to find the number of sultanas per 2 scones e.g. 75 ÷ 5 (= 15) or per 1 scone e.g. 75 ÷ 10 (= 7.5); 1 mark for correct answer of 90 grams.*

**5.** Top row: £3.00  (£6.00)  £16.50
Bottom row: £2.25  £4.50  £12.38
*1 mark for method to find at least one cost from top row e.g. £6 ÷ 2 (= £3) or a correct entry in the table; 1 mark for method to find at least one cost from bottom row e.g. £6 ÷ 4 × 3 (= £4.50) or a correct entry in this row; 1 mark for a fully correct table. Total 3 marks.*

**6.** 5 : 12 : 13 = 1 : 2.4 : 2.6 = 2 : 4.8 : 5.2
Perimeter = 2 + 4.8 + 5.2 = 12 cm
*1 mark for method to find at least one of the missing sides e.g. 12 ÷ 5 × 2 (= 4.8) or 13 ÷ 5 × 2 (= 5.2); 1 mark for adding all three sides; 1 mark for correct answer of 12 cm. Total 3 marks.*
*Note that there are alternative methods.*

## Page 52, Using ratio

**1.** 8 + 1 = 9 parts
Each part = 270 ÷ 9 = 30
Water = 8 × 30 = 240 ml
*1 mark for correct answer circled.*

**2.** $11 + 3 = 14$ parts

Each part $= 70 \div 14 = 5$

Winning cards $= 11 \times 5 = 55$

***1 mark*** *for $70 \div 14$ (= 5);* ***1 mark*** *for correct answer of 55*

**3.** 3 parts = 9 litres

Each part $= 9 \div 3 = 1$ litre

White paint $= 2 \times 1 = 2$ litres

***1 mark*** *for $9 \div 3$ (= 3);* ***1 mark*** *for correct answer of 2 litres.*

**4.** $3 + 4$ parts = 7 parts

Each part $= 98 \div 7 = 14$

The shorter paper has 3 parts.

Shorter paper $= 3 \times 14 = 42$

***1 mark*** *for $98 \div 37$ (= 14);* ***1 mark*** *for correct answer of 42*

**5. a** Isosceles

  ***1 mark*** *for correct answer.*

 **b** $3 + 2 + 3 = 8$ parts

Each part $= 180° \div 8 = 22.5°$

Smallest angle $= 2 \times 22.5 = 45°$

***1 mark*** *for dividing 180 by the sum of 3, 2 and 3;* ***1 mark*** *for 22.5;* ***1 mark*** *for correct answer of 45°. Total 3 marks.*

**Alternative solution:**

$3 + 2 + 3 = 8$ parts

Size of smallest angle $= \frac{2}{8} \times 180°$

$= \frac{1}{4} \times 180°$

$= 45°$

***1 mark*** *for finding $\frac{2}{8}$ or $\frac{1}{4}$;* ***1 mark*** *for multiplying by 180;* ***1 mark*** *for correct answer of 45°. Total 3 marks. Note that there are other alternative methods.*

**6.** $7 - 2 = 5$

5 parts = 90

1 part = 18

$7 \times 18 = 126$ pencils

***1 mark*** *for dividing 90 by 5 (= 18);* ***1 mark*** *for correct answer.*

## Page 53, Percentage change

**1.** 3% of £50 000 $= £50 000 \div 100 \times 3 = £1500$

New value $= £50 000 + £1500 = £51 500$

***1 mark*** *for 50 000 + (50 000 ÷ 100 × 3) or equivalent e.g. 50 000 × 1.03;* ***1 mark*** *for correct answer of £51 500*

**2.** Actual decrease $= 4 - 2.5 = 1.5$

% decrease $= \frac{1.5 \times 100\%}{4} = \frac{150\%}{4} = \frac{75\%}{2} = 37.5\%$

***1 mark*** *for $\frac{4 - 2.5}{4} \times 100\%$;* ***1 mark*** *for correct answer of 37.5%.*

**3.** Actual increase $= 5 - 4 = 1$

% increase $= \frac{1 \times 100\%}{4} = 25\%$

***1 mark*** *for correct answer circled. Note 1 is the increase in cm not % and 20% is from using the new length as the denominator when you need to use the original length.*

**4.** Total Maths score = 280

15% of 280 (= 10% + 5%) $= 28 + 14 = 42$

Total English score $= 280 - 42 = 238$

Missing English score $= 238 - (58 + 58 + 57)$

$= 238 - 173 = 65$

***1 mark*** *for 280;* ***1 mark*** *for correct method to find 15% of 280 <u>and</u> subtract;* ***1 mark*** *for subtracting 173;* ***1 mark*** *for correct answer of 65. Total 4 marks.*

**5.** Actual increase in age $= 12 - 10 = 2$

% increase in age $= \frac{2 \times 100\%}{10} = 20\%$

Therefore, age increases by 20%.

20% of 20 kg = 4 kg

Talia's dog's mass at 12 $= 20 + 4 = 24$ kg

***1 mark*** *for $\frac{12 - 10}{10} \times 100\%$;* ***1 mark*** *for 20%;* ***1 mark*** *for 20 + 20% of 20;* ***1 mark*** *for correct answer of 24 kg. Total 4 marks.*

## Page 54, Multipliers

**1.** 40%

***1 mark*** *for correct answer circled. Remember $0.4 = \frac{4}{10} = \frac{40}{100} = 40\%$.*

**2. a** Multiplier for 10% increase = 1.1

New value $= 50 \times 1.1 = 55$

 **b** Multiplier for 55% decrease = 0.45

New value $= 40 \times 0.45 = 18$

***1 mark*** *for each correct multiplier;* ***1 mark*** *for each correct answer. Note that other methods score no marks, as the question states that a multiplier must be used.*

**3.** Multiplier for 7% decrease = 0.93

Next ball speed $= 90 \times 0.93 = 83.7$ mph

***1 mark*** *for 0.93;* ***1 mark*** *for correct answer of 83.7 mph. Note that other methods score no marks, as the question states that a multiplier must be used.*

**4. a** 6% of £2450 $= £2450 \div 100 \times 6 = £147$

Total interest for 2 years $= £147 \times 2 = £294$

Amount in bank $= £2450 + £294 = £2744$

***1 mark*** *for correct method to find 6% of £2450 e.g. 2450 ÷ 100 × 6 (= 147);* ***1 mark*** *for multiplying your answer by 2 (= 294);* ***1 mark*** *for correct final answer of £2744. Total 3 marks.*

 **b** Multiplier for 6% = 1.06

1st year $= £2450 \times 1.06 = £2597$

2nd year $= £2597 \times 1.06 = £2752.82$

***1 mark*** *for 1.06;* ***1 mark*** *for multiplying £2450 by 1.06 (= £2597) or for multiplying by $1.06^2$;* ***1 mark*** *for correct final answer of £2752.82. Total 3 marks.*

**5.** Multiplier for 4% decrease = 0.96

1st year $= 3000 000 \times 0.96 = 2880 000$

2nd year $= 2880 000 \times 0.96 = 2764 800$

***1 mark*** *for 0.96;* ***1 mark*** *for at least one step of multiplying a population by 0.96 or for multiplying by $0.96^2$;* ***1 mark*** *for correct final answer of 2764 800. Total 3 marks.*

## Page 55, Original value problems

**1.** 70% = 0.7

£28 ÷ 0.7 = £40

***1 mark*** *for 0.7;* ***1 mark*** *for dividing by 0.7;* ***1 mark*** *for correct answer of £40. Total 3 marks.*

**Alternative solution:**

100% − 30% = 70%

70% = £28

10% = £4

Original price = 100% = £4 × 10 = £40

***1 mark*** *for 70%;* ***1 mark*** *for dividing by 7 and multiplying by 10;* ***1 mark*** *for correct answer of £40. Total 3 marks.*

**2.** 115% = 1.15

23 miles ÷ 1.15 = 20 miles

***1 mark*** *for 1.15;* ***1 mark*** *for dividing by 1.15;* ***1 mark*** *for correct answer of 20 miles. Total 3 marks.*

**3.** 120% = 1.20

£92.40 ÷ 1.20 = £77

*1 mark for 1.20 (or 1.2); 1 mark for dividing by 1.20; 1 mark for correct answer of £77. Total 3 marks.*

**4.** 89% = 0.89

44.5 grams ÷ 0.89 = 50 grams

*1 mark for 0.89; 1 mark for dividing by 0.89; 1 mark for correct answer of 50 grams. Total 3 marks.*

**5.** 103% = 1.03

£278.10 ÷ 1.03 = £270

*1 mark for 1.03; 1 mark for dividing by 1.03; 1 mark for correct answer of £270. Total 3 marks.*

**6.** 120% = 1.20 and 80% = 0.80

Let the original number be $x$.

20% increase = $x \times 1.20 = 1.20x$

20% decrease = $1.20x \times 0.80 = 0.96x$ ($< x$)

The original number is $x$, so the answer is less than the original number.

*1 mark for either 1.20 or 0.80; 1 mark for attempt to multiply any number (algebra not necessary) by 1.20 and 0.80; 1 mark for complete and correct argument. Total 3 marks.*

## Page 56, Compound measures

**1.** Time = distance ÷ speed = 1020 ÷ 30 = 34 seconds

*1 mark for attempt to use correct formula; 1 mark for correct answer including units.*

**2.** Rate of pay = total pay ÷ hours worked

= 368 ÷ 32 = £11.50 per hour

*1 mark for attempt to use correct formula; 1 mark for correct answer including units.*

**3.** Time = 2400 ÷ 20 = 120 seconds

*1 mark for 2400 ÷ 20; 1 mark for correct answer including units (or equivalent e.g. 2 minutes).*

**4.** Mass = density × volume = 8.94 × 0.6 = 5.364 g

*1 mark for correct answer circled.*

**5.** Pressure = force ÷ area = 36 ÷ 0.45 = 80 N/m² (or 80 Pa)

*1 mark for attempt to use correct formula; 1 mark for correct answer including units.*

**6.** 38 700 000 g = 38 700 kg

Density = mass ÷ volume = 38 700 ÷ 5 = 7740 kg/m³

*1 mark for dividing by 1000 to change g to kg; 1 mark for attempt to use correct formula; 1 mark for correct answer including units. Total 3 marks.*

**7. a** 0.047 km/h = 47 m/h = 0.783… m/min

Time = distance ÷ speed = 5.64 ÷ 0.783…

= 7.2 minutes = 7 minutes and 12 seconds

*1 mark for at least one of multiplying by 1000 (to change km/h to m/h) or dividing by 60 (to change m/h to m/min); 1 mark for attempt to use correct formula to find the time; 1 mark for 7.2; 1 mark for correct answer of 7 minutes and 12 seconds. Total 4 marks.*

*Note that there are alternative methods.*

**b** 0.78 m/min = 46.8 m/h = 0.0468 km/h

0.047 > 0.0468, so garden snail is faster.

*1 mark for at least one of multiplying by 60 (to change m/min to m/h) or dividing by 1000 (to change m/h to km/h); 1 mark for 0.0468; 1 mark for comparing correct values with correct conclusion (i.e. snail faster). Total 3 marks.*

## Page 57, Direct proportion

**1. a** 3.5 pints      **b** Between 2.2 litres and 2.3 litres

*2 marks for each correct answer (1 mark for each line drawn on graph).*

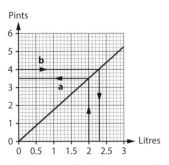

**2. a** Yes    **b** No    **c** Yes    **d** No

*1 mark for each correct answer.*

**3. a** Missing values from left to right: 0, 1.5

*1 mark for 0; 1 mark for 1.5*

**b** $y = 1.5x$ or $\frac{3}{2}x$

*1 mark for correct answer.*

**4. a** 9 ÷ 3 × 4 = 12

*1 mark for dividing by 3 and multiplying by 4; 1 mark for correct answer of 12*

**b** 21 ÷ 3 = 7

*1 mark for dividing by 3; 1 mark for correct answer.*

**c** $y = 3x$

*1 mark for correct answer (or equivalent e.g. $x = \frac{y}{3}$).*

**5.** 'Dogs Love Bach' sell 9 kg for £12.99

12.99 ÷ 9 = £1.44… per 1 kg

'Woof & Ready' sell 8 kg for £11.00

11.00 ÷ 8 = £1.375 per 1 kg

'Woof & Ready' offers better value.

*1 mark for at least one of dividing costs by 9 or 8; 1 mark for £1.44… or £1.375; 1 mark for comparison of correct answers with correct conclusion (i.e. 'Woof & Ready' cheaper). Total 3 marks.*

*Note that there are alternative methods.*

## Page 58, Inverse proportion

**1. a** 12 × 6 = 72 'builder days'

72 ÷ 18 = 4 days

*1 mark for 12 × 6 ÷ 18 or equivalent e.g. 6 ÷ (18 ÷ 12); 1 mark for correct answer of 4 days.*

**b** 72 ÷ 3 = 24 builders

*1 mark for 12 × 6 ÷ 3 or equivalent e.g. 12 × (6 ÷ 3); 1 mark for correct answer of 24 builders.*

**2. a** 3 × 30 = 90 hours of pumping water

90 ÷ 4 = 22.5 hours

*1 mark for 3 × 30 ÷ 4 or equivalent e.g. 30 ÷ (4 ÷ 3); 1 mark for correct answer of 22.5 hours.*

**b** 90 ÷ 10 = 9 hosepipes

*1 mark for 3 × 30 ÷ 10 or equivalent e.g. 3 × (30 ÷ 10); 1 mark for correct answer of 9 hosepipes.*

**3. B**

*1 mark for correct answer circled.*

**4. a** $y = \frac{6}{x}$

**b** $y = \frac{6}{4} = \frac{3}{2}$ or 1.5

**c** $x = \frac{6}{1} = 6$

*1 mark for each correct answer.*

## Page 59, Time and timetables

**1. a** 6:35 am

*1 mark for correct answer, including am.*

**b** 17:20

*1 mark for correct answer (no marks if am or pm used).*

**2.** 7:31 pm + 2 hours 15 minutes = 9:46 pm

8:24 pm to 9:46 pm is 1 hour and 22 minutes.

There is 1 hour and 22 minutes left.

*1 mark for 9:46; 1 mark for correct answer.*

**3. a** $0.4 \times 60 = 24$

3.4 hours = 3 hours and 24 minutes

*1 mark for correct answer circled.*

**b** $48 \div 60 = 0.8$

1 hour 48 minutes = 1.8 hours

*1 mark for dividing 48 by 60 (= 0.8); 1 mark for correct answer.*

**4. a** 15:40

*1 mark for correct answer.*

**b** The 12:20 from Aust arrives at Brant at 12:35

12:35 + 10 min + 2 hours 45 min + 10 min = 15:40

The next bus from Brant is at 15:50

Therefore, he arrives back at Aust at 16:05

*1 mark for 12:35; 1 mark for adding all times together (or 15:40); 1 mark for correct final answer of 16:05. Total 3 marks.*

## Page 60, Measures

**1. a** Line drawn with length 5.4 cm (i.e. 54 mm)

*1 mark for correct length of line.*

**b** Line measurements are 51 mm, 85 mm and 108 mm.

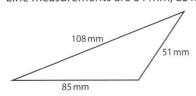

Total perimeter = 244 mm

*1 mark for correct length of any line; 1 mark for correct answer.*

**2. a** Millimetres (mm) or centimetres (cm)

**b** Grams (g)  **c** Millilitres (ml) or centilitres (cl)

*1 mark for each correct final answer.*

**3.** $17 \times 10 = 170$ mm

*1 mark for correct answer circled.*

**4. a** $2500 \div 1000 = 2.5$ g

**b** $0.35 \times 1000 = 350$ ml

*1 mark for each correct answer.*

**5.** Sugar: $36 \times 28 = 1008$ g

$1008 \div 1000 = 1.008$ kg

Flour: $2 \times 0.45 = 0.9$ kg

Total weight = 0.9 + 1.008 = 1.908 kg

*1 mark for $36 \times 28 \div 1000$ (= 1.008); 1 mark for $2 \times 0.45$ (= 0.9); 1 mark for correct final answer. Total 3 marks.*

**6.** 5 feet = 60 inches

68 inches = 5 feet 8 inches

*1 mark for 5 feet; 1 mark for correct answer.*

## Page 61, Scale drawing

**1. a** 1.8 m to 2.2 m

**b** 1 m : 3 cm

6 m : 6 × 3 = 18 cm

*1 mark for each correct answer.*

**2.** $184 \times 100 = 18\,400$ cm

$18\,400 \div 2000 = 9.2$ cm

*1 mark for correct answer circled.*

**3. a** 2 cm : 5 km = 2 cm : 5000 m = 2 cm : 500 000 cm

= 1 : 250 000

*1 mark for 500 000 cm; 1 mark for correct answer.*

**b** $5 \times 400\,000 = 2\,000\,000$ cm = 20 000 m = 20 km

*1 mark for 2 000 000 cm; 1 mark for correct answer.*

**4.** $30.5 \div 5 = 6.1$

6.1 cm represents 30.5 m.

$15.25 \div 5 = 3.05$ (or $6.1 \div 2 = 3.05$)

3.05 cm represents 15.25 m.

*1 mark for $30.5 \div 5$ (= 6.1) or $15.25 \div 5$ (= 3.05); 1 mark for 6.1 and 3.05 correct; 1 mark for rectangle drawn with length 6.1 cm and width 3.05 cm. Total 3 marks.*

## Page 62, Angles

**1. a** Right, acute, reflex

*1 mark for each correct answer. Total 3 marks.*

**b** Straight angle (or straight line)

*1 mark for correct answer.*

**2. a** 134° drawn

e.g.

*1 mark for correct angle drawn.*

**b** Obtuse

*1 mark for correct answer.*

**3.** Acute $ABC = 80°$

Reflex $ABC = 360° - 80° = 280°$

*1 mark for 80°; 2 marks for 280°.*

**4.** e.g. 10° (acute) + 20° (acute) = 30° (acute)

*1 mark for any clear adding of two acute angles to create another acute angle (or right angle).*

## Page 63, Angle rules

**1.** $x + 151° = 180°$

$x = 180° - 151°$

$= 29°$

*1 mark for $x + 151 = 180$ or $180 - 151$; 1 mark for correct answer.*

**2.** $360° \div 3 = 120°$

The hour hand turns 120°.

*1 mark for correct answer circled. Remember there are 360° in the whole circle; the hand moves 4 out of 12 equal parts of this i.e. one third of 360°.*

**3. a** $a = 120°$. Alternate angles (are equal).

**b** $b = 115°$. Corresponding angles (are equal).

*1 mark for each correct angle; 1 mark for each correct reason.*

**4.** $3y + 10° = y + 30°$

$2y = 20°$

$y = 10°$

*1 mark for $3y + 10 = y + 30$; 1 mark for a correct algebraic step e.g. $2y + 10 = 30$; 1 mark for correct answer. Total 3 marks.*

## Page 64, Bearings

**1. a** 090°

*1 mark for correct answer. Must be 3 figures.*

**b.** 180°

*1 mark for correct answer.*

**2.** $180° + 130° = 310°$
Bearing is 310°.
***1 mark*** *for 180 + 130 (= 310);* ***1 mark*** *for correct answer.*

**3. a** 060°
***1 mark*** *for 060°. Must be 3 figures.*

**b**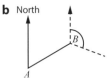
***1 mark*** *for line drawn on a bearing of 110°.*

**4.** $180° – 30° = 150°$
$90° + 150° = 240°$
Bearing is 240°.
***1 mark*** *for subtracting 30;* ***1 mark*** *for correct final answer. Note that there are alternative methods.*

**5.**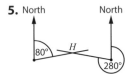
***1 mark*** *for either 080° bearing or 280° bearing drawn correctly;* ***1 mark*** *for both bearings drawn correctly;* ***1 mark*** *for correct lines intersecting and labelled H. Total 3 marks.*

## Page 65, Triangles & quadrilaterals

**1.** Trapezium
***1 mark*** *for correct answer circled.*

**2.** $180° – 42° = 138°$
$138° ÷ 2 = 69°$
$y = 69°$
***1 mark*** *for (180 – 42) ÷ 2;* ***1 mark*** *for correct answer.*

**3.** Angles on a straight line add up to 180°.
Angle $ABC = 180° – 95° = 85°$
Opposite angles of a rhombus are equal.
Therefore, $x = 85°$.
***1 mark*** *for each correct reason stated;* ***1 mark*** *for correct answer of 85°. Total 3 marks. Alternative solutions may include angle rules for parallel lines (e.g. corresponding angles, alternate angles).*

**4.** Angles in a quadrilateral add up to 360°.
$x + 2x + 3x + 2x + 20° = 360°$
$8x + 20° = 360°$
$8x = 340°$
Therefore, $x = 42.5°$, which is the smallest angle.
***1 mark*** *for forming correct equation;* ***1 mark*** *for any correct algebraic step (e.g. x + 2x + 2x + 3x = 360 – 20 etc.);* ***1 mark*** *for correct answer of 42.5°. Total 3 marks.*

**5.** Angle $EAD = 44°$ (alternate angles)
Angle $FDE = 180° – 90° – 44° = 46°$
(Angles in triangle add up to 180°.)
***1 mark*** *for angle EAD = 44;* ***1 mark*** *for 180 – 90 – angle EAD;* ***1 mark*** *for correct final answer. Total 3 marks.*

## Page 66, Polygons

**1. a** Pentagon
***1 mark*** *for correct answer circled.*

**b** All of its angles are equal, and all of its sides have equal length.
***1 mark*** *for correct answer.*

**2.** $360° ÷ 60° = 6$
The shape is a (regular) hexagon.

***1 mark*** *for 360 ÷ 60 (= 6) or for stating that exterior angles add up to 360°;* ***1 mark*** *for hexagon.*

**3.** Interior angle sum is $(6 – 2) × 180° = 720°$
$41° + 59° + 83° + 90° + 147° = 420°$
$720° – 420° = 300°$
***1 mark*** *for (6 – 2) × 180 (= 720);* ***1 mark*** *for adding all angles and subtracting the total from your 720;* ***1 mark*** *for correct answer of 300°. Total 3 marks.*

**4.** $(8 – 2) × 180° = 1080°$
$1080° ÷ 8 = 135°$ (= angle in octagon)
$x = 360° – 60°$ (equilateral triangle) $– 90°$ (square) $– 135°$ (octagon) $= 75°$
***1 mark*** *for (8 – 2) × 180 (= 1080);* ***1 mark*** *for 1080 ÷ 8 (= 135);* ***1 mark*** *for subtracting your 3 angles from 360;* ***1 mark*** *for correct final answer of 75°. If no marks scored, score* ***1 mark*** *for 60 (equilateral triangle) or 90 (square). Total 4 marks.*

**5.** Exterior angle $= 180° – 80° = 100°$
$360° ÷ 100° = 3.6$
A regular polygon cannot have 3.6 sides, so Sophia is correct.
***1 mark*** *for 180 – 80 (= 100);* ***1 mark*** *for 360 ÷ 100 (= 3.6);* ***1 mark*** *for concluding that Sophia is correct with full explanation. Total 3 marks.*

**Alternative solution:**
An equilateral triangle (regular 3-sided polygon) has interior angles of size 60°.
A square (regular 4-sided polygon) has interior angles of size 90°.
As $60° < 80° < 90°$, there can be no regular polygon with an interior angle of 80°.
***1 mark*** *for attempt at comparison with regular 3 and 4-sided polygons;* ***1 mark*** *for 60 and 90;* ***1 mark*** *for concluding that Sophia is correct with full explanation. Total 3 marks.*

## Page 67, Reflection

**1. a**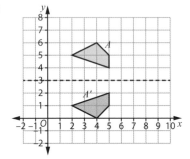
***1 mark*** *for image drawn with correct size and orientation;* ***1 mark*** *for fully correct.*

**b** $y = 3$
***1 mark*** *for correct answer.*

**2.** Reflection in the line $x = –1$
***1 mark*** *for 'reflection' or 'x = –1';* ***1 mark*** *for fully correct.*

**3. a**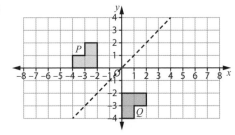
***1 mark*** *for image drawn with correct size and orientation;* ***1 mark*** *for fully correct.*

**b** $y = x$

*1 mark for correct answer.*

## Page 68, Rotation

**1.** $(-1, -2)$

*1 mark for correct answer circled.*

**2. a**

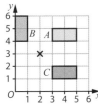

*1 mark for a rectangle drawn with correct size and orientation; 1 mark for correct answer.*

**b** Rotation of 180° about (4, 3)

*1 mark for 180°; 1 mark for (4, 3).*

**3. a**

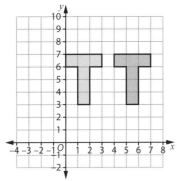

*1 mark for a triangle drawn with correct size and orientation; 1 mark for correct answer.*

**b** Triangle $T$

*1 mark for correct answer.*

## Page 69, Translation

**1.** $\begin{pmatrix} -3 \\ 4 \end{pmatrix}$

*1 mark for correct answer circled.*

**2.**

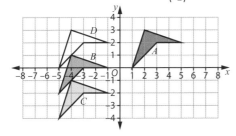

*1 mark for T-shape drawn in correct position.*

**3. a** Translation $\begin{pmatrix} -6 \\ -2 \end{pmatrix}$

*1 mark for translation; 1 mark for $\begin{pmatrix} -6 \\ -2 \end{pmatrix}$.*

**b i**

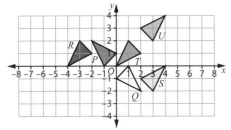

*1 mark for shape $D$ drawn in correct position.*

**ii** Translation $\begin{pmatrix} 0 \\ -2 \end{pmatrix}$

*1 mark for translation; 1 mark for $\begin{pmatrix} 0 \\ -2 \end{pmatrix}$.*

**4.** Finbar is correct as the column vector $\begin{pmatrix} 0 \\ 0 \end{pmatrix}$ represents zero movement in both horizontal and vertical directions.

*1 mark for correct conclusion (Finbar is correct) with clear explanation.*

## Page 70, Enlargement

**1.** Shape $B$

*1 mark for correct answer circled. Remember in maths an enlargement with scale factor between 0 and 1 gives a smaller shape.*

**2.** Enlargement by scale factor 3 with centre of enlargement $(-2, 0)$

*1 mark for enlargement; 1 mark for scale factor 3; 1 mark for (–2, 0). Total 3 marks.*

**3. a–b**

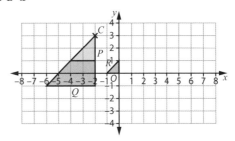

*For part **a**, 1 mark for enlargement with scale factor 2 anywhere in the grid; 1 mark for correct position of enlarged triangle.*

*For part **b**, 1 mark for an enlargement with scale factor $\frac{1}{2}$ anywhere in the grid; 1 mark for correct position.*

## Page 71, Congruent shapes

**1.** $B$

*1 mark for correct shape circled.*

**2.**

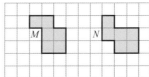

*1 mark for 3 correct squares shaded. (There are many possible correct answers.)*

**3. a** RHS   **b** SSS   **c** SAS

*1 mark for each correct answer.*

**4. a** 24 cm (It corresponds to $AC$.)

**b** 75° (It corresponds to angle $DFE$.)

*1 mark for each correct answer.*

## Page 72, Similar shapes

**1.** $C$

*1 mark for correct shape circled.*

**2.** $\frac{y}{24} = \frac{40}{16}$

$y = \frac{40 \times 24}{16} = 60$ cm

*1 mark for equating suitable ratios of sides e.g. $\frac{24}{y} = \frac{16}{40}$ or $\frac{24}{16} = \frac{y}{40}$; 1 mark for correct answer.*

**3.** $\frac{19.5}{13} = \frac{18}{12} = \frac{7.5}{5} = 1.5$

Scale factor is 1.5

Therefore, triangles are similar.

*1 mark* for comparing ratios of at least 2 pairs of sides (also accept $\frac{13}{19.5} = \frac{12}{18} = \frac{5}{7.5} = \frac{2}{3}$); *1 mark* for scale factor 1.5 or $\frac{2}{3}$ with conclusion.

*Note that there are alternative methods.*

**4.** $\frac{AC}{AB} = \frac{AD}{AE}$

$\frac{11.5}{9.2} = \frac{AD}{8.4}$

$AD = \frac{11.5 \times 8.4}{9.2} = 10.5$

$ED = AD - AE = 10.5 - 8.4 = 2.1$ cm

*1 mark* for comparing ratios of 2 pairs of sides e.g. $\frac{AB}{AE} = \frac{AC}{AD}$; *1 mark* for correct answer of 2.1 cm.

*Note that there are alternative methods.*

## Page 73, Area and perimeter

**1. a** Area $= \frac{1}{2} \times (6 + 9) \times 4 = 30$ cm²

   *1 mark* for correct calculation; *1 mark* for correct answer. (Also accept $6 \times 4 + \frac{1}{2} \times 3 \times 4$ for method.)

   **b** Area $= \frac{1}{2} \times 6 \times 4 = 12$ cm²

   *1 mark* for correct calculation; *1 mark* for correct answer.

   **c** Area $= 25 \times 12 = 300$ cm²

   *1 mark* for correct calculation; *1 mark* for correct answer.

**2.** Length of rectangle $= 12$ cm

Perimeter $= 6 + 6 + 12 + 12 = 36$ cm

*1 mark* for length of 12 cm; *1 mark* for correct answer.

**3.** $125 + 125 + x - 4 + x - 4 = 380$

$2x + 242 = 380$

$2x = 138$

$x = 69$

Perimeter of £10 note

$= 132 + 132 + 69 + 69 = 402$ mm

*1 mark* for forming an equation in $x$ for the perimeter of the £5 note; *1 mark* for 69; *1 mark* for correct answer of 402 mm. Total 3 marks.

**4.** $12.8x = \frac{1}{2} \times 12.8 \times 17.9$

$x = \frac{1}{2} \times 17.9 = 8.95$ cm

*1 mark* for using formulae for area of triangle and of parallelogram; *1 mark* for correct answer.

## Page 74, Compound shapes

**1. a** Missing side $= 11$ m $- 3$ m $= 8$ m

   Perimeter $= 8 + 5 + 8 + 4 + 11 = 36$ m

   *1 mark* for missing side *1 mark* for correct answer.

   **b** Triangle area $= \frac{1}{2} \times 3 \times 4 = 6$ m²

   Rectangle area $= 4 \times 11 = 44$ m²

   Compound area $= 6 + 44 = 50$ m²

   *1 mark* for $\frac{1}{2} \times 3 \times 4$ ($= 6$ m²); *1 mark* for $4 \times 11$ ($= 44$ m²); *1 mark* for correct answer. Total 3 marks.

**2**

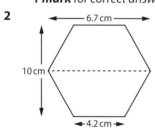

Area of trapezium $= \frac{1}{2} \times (4.2 + 6.7) \times 5$

$= 27.25$ cm²

Area of hexagon $= 2 \times 27.25 = 54.5$ cm²

*1 mark* for $\frac{1}{2} \times (4.2 + 6.7) \times 5$ ($= 27.25$); *1 mark* for correct answer.

*Note that there are alternative methods.*

**3.**

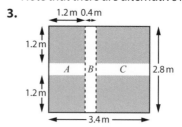

Area $A = 1.2 \times 0.4 = 0.48$ m²

Area $B = 2.8 \times 0.4 = 1.12$ m²

Area $C = 1.8 \times 0.4 = 0.72$ m²

Total white cross area $= 0.48 + 1.12 + 0.72 = 2.32$ m²

*1 mark* for any correct rectangle area; *1 mark* for all rectangle areas correct; *1 mark* for final answer. Total 3 marks.

*Note that there are alternative methods.*

## Page 75, Circles

**1. a** Area $= \pi \times 3^2 = 9\pi$ mm² $= 28.3$ mm² to 3 sf

   *1 mark* for correct calculation; *1 mark* for $9\pi$ or $28.27\ldots$; *1 mark* for correct answer to 3 sf. Total 3 marks.

   **b** Circumference $= 2 \times \pi \times 3 = 6\pi$ mm $= 18.8$ mm to 3 sf

   *1 mark* for correct calculation (also accept $\pi \times 6$); *1 mark* for $6\pi$ or $18.84\ldots$; *1 mark* for correct answer to 3 sf. Total 3 marks.

**2. a** Tangent

   *1 mark* for correct answer.

   Segment

   *1 mark* for correct answer.

   **b**

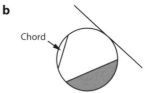

   *1 mark* for any line segment drawn connecting two points on the circle (but not passing through the centre).

**3. a** Area $= \pi \times 4^2 = 16\pi$ cm²

   *1 mark* for correct calculation; *1 mark* for correct answer.

   **b** Circumference $= \pi \times 8 = 8\pi$ cm

   *1 mark* for correct calculation (also accept $2 \times \pi \times 4$); *1 mark* for correct answer.

**4.** Let $r$ be the radius.

Area $= \pi r^2 = 25\pi$

$r^2 = 25$

$r = 5$ cm

Circumference $= 2 \times \pi \times 5 = 10\pi$ cm

*1 mark* for $r = 5$; *1 mark* for final answer of $10\pi$ cm or $31.4\ldots$ cm.

**5.** Area of original circle $= \pi r^2$

If radius halved, then new area $= \pi \left(\frac{1}{2}r\right)^2 = \frac{1}{4}\pi r^2$

Hyacinth is not correct. The area is one quarter of the area of the original circle.

*1 mark* for using $\frac{1}{2}r$ for radius of new circle; *1 mark* for $\frac{1}{4}r^2$; *1 mark* for concluding that Hyacinth is incorrect with justification. Total 3 marks.

*Note that there are alternative methods.*

## Page 76, Semicircles

**1. a i** Area $= \frac{\pi r^2}{2} = \frac{\pi \times 4.5^2}{2} = 31.8\,\text{cm}^2$

*1 mark for $\frac{\pi \times 4.5^2}{2}$; 1 mark for correct answer to 1 dp.*

**ii** Perimeter $= \frac{\pi d}{2} + d = \frac{\pi \times 9}{2} + 9 = 23.1\,\text{cm}$

*1 mark for $\frac{\pi \times 9}{2} + 9$; 1 mark for correct answer to 1 dp.*

**b i** Area $= \frac{\pi r^2}{2} = \frac{\pi \times 5^2}{2} = \frac{25\pi}{2} = 39.3\,\text{cm}^2$

*1 mark for $\frac{\pi \times 5^2}{2}$; $\left(= \frac{25\pi}{2}\right)$; 1 mark for correct answer to 3 sf; 1 mark for correct units. Total 3 marks.*

**ii** Perimeter $= \frac{\pi d}{2} + d = \frac{\pi \times 10}{2} + 10 = 25.7\,\text{cm}$

*1 mark for $\frac{\pi \times 10}{2} + 10$; 1 mark for correct answer to 3 sf; 1 mark for correct units. Total 3 marks.*

**2.** Large semicircle diameter $= 19.3 + 4.9 = 24.2\,\text{m}$

Perimeter $= \frac{\pi \times 24.2}{2} + \frac{\pi \times 19.3}{2} + \frac{\pi \times 4.9}{2} = 76.0\,\text{m}$

*1 mark for $\frac{\pi \times 24.2}{2}$ (= 38.013...) or $\frac{\pi \times 19.3}{2}$ (= 30.316...) or $\frac{\pi \times 4.9}{2}$ (= 7.696...); 1 mark for adding perimeters of all 3 semicircles; 1 mark for final answer correct to 3 sf. Total 3 marks.*

**3.** Area of semicircle $= \frac{\pi r^2}{2} = \frac{\pi \times 5.5^2}{2}$ (= 47.516...)

Height of trapezium $= 10 - \frac{11}{2} = 4.5$

Area of trapezium $= \frac{1}{2} \times (11 + 7) \times 4.5 = 40.5$

Area of compound shape $= 47.516... + 40.5 = 88.0\,\text{cm}^2$

*1 mark for $\frac{\pi \times 5.5^2}{2}$ (= 47.516...); 1 mark for finding the trapezium height; 1 mark for $\frac{1}{2} \times (11 + 7) \times 4.5$ (= 40.5); 1 mark for correct answer to 1 dp. Total 4 marks.*

## Page 77, Arcs and sectors

**1. a** Area $= \pi r^2 \times \frac{\theta^\circ}{360^\circ} = \pi \times 15^2 \times \frac{50^\circ}{360^\circ} = 98.2\,\text{cm}^2$

*1 mark for $\pi \times 15^2 \times \frac{50}{360}$; 1 mark for correct answer to 1 dp; 1 mark for correct units. Total 3 marks.*

**b** Arc length $= 2\pi r \times \frac{\theta^\circ}{360^\circ} = 2 \times \pi \times 15 \times \frac{50^\circ}{360^\circ} = 13.1\,\text{cm}$

*1 mark for $2 \times \pi \times 15 \times \frac{50}{360}$; 1 mark for correct answer to 1 dp; 1 mark for correct units. Total 3 marks.*

**2. a** Area $= \pi \times 13^2 \times \frac{200^\circ}{360^\circ} = 295.0\,\text{cm}^2$

**b** Arc length $= 2 \times \pi \times 13 \times \frac{200^\circ}{360^\circ} = 45.4\,\text{cm}$

*For each part, 1 mark for using correct formula; 1 mark for correct answer to 1 dp.*

**3. a** 60°

*1 mark for correct answer.*

**b** Area $= \pi r^2 \times \frac{\theta^\circ}{360^\circ} = \pi \times 18^2 \times \frac{60^\circ}{360^\circ} = 54\pi\,\text{cm}^2$

*1 mark for $\pi \times 18^2 \times \frac{60}{360}$; 1 mark for $54\pi$.*

**4. a** Arc length $= 2 \times \pi \times 8 \times \frac{3}{4} = 12\pi\,\text{cm}$

**b** Area $= \pi \times 8^2 \times \frac{3}{4} = 48\pi\,\text{cm}^2$

*For each part, 1 mark for using correct formula; 1 mark for correct answer in terms of $\pi$.*

## Page 78, 3D shapes

**1. a** Triangular-based pyramid

*1 mark for 'pyramid' or 'triangular pyramid' or 'triangular-based pyramid' or 'tetrahedron' but not 'square-based pyramid' etc.*

**b** Triangular prism

*1 mark for 'prism' or 'triangular prism' but not for other types of prism.*

**c** Cone

*1 mark for correct answer.*

**2. a** Cuboid

*1 mark for correct answer circled. Remember rectangles and squares are 2D shapes.*

**b i** 6    **ii** 8    **iii** 12

*1 mark for each correct answer.*

**3.** 7 faces, 15 edges, 10 vertices

*1 mark for each correct answer. Total 3 marks.*

**4. a** Any correct face, for example:

*1 mark for shading any correct face (including those not indicated here).*

**b** Any correct face, for example:

*1 mark for circling any correct vertex (including those not indicated here).*

**c** Number of faces = 5

Number of vertices = 5

Number of edges = 8

$5 + 5 - 8 = 2$

*1 mark for correct number of faces, vertices or edges; 1 mark for correct final answer of 2*

## Page 79, Plans and elevations

**1.**

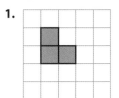 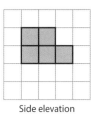 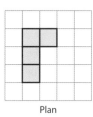

Front elevation      Side elevation      Plan

*1 mark for each correct diagram; note the plan can be in any orientation as long as it's from above. Total 3 marks.*

**2. a**

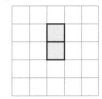

*1 mark for correct diagram in any orientation.*

**b**

*1 mark for a correct 3D drawing of an 'L-shape'; 1 mark for fully correct diagram.*

**Page 80, Nets and surface area**

**1. C**

*1 mark for correct answer circled. Think about folding the net round and which parts would become the top, sides and bottom faces of the cube.*

**2. a** Cuboid

*1 mark for correct answer.*

**b** $(4 \times 8) + (4 \times 2) + (2 \times 8) = 56$
$2 \times 56 = 112\,\text{cm}^2$
*1 mark for $4 \times 8\ (= 32)$ or $4 \times 2\ (= 8)$ or $2 \times 8\ (= 16)$;*
*1 mark for 112; 1 mark for $\text{cm}^2$. Total 3 marks.*
*Note that there are alternative methods.*

**3. a**

 or

*1 mark for an attempt involving exactly 4 equilateral triangles; 1 mark for either of the above nets correctly drawn in any orientation.*

**b** Area of each triangle $= \frac{1}{2} \times 3 \times 2.6 = 3.9$
Total surface area $= 4 \times 3.9 = 15.6\,\text{cm}^2$
*1 mark for $\frac{1}{2} \times 3 \times 2.6\ (= 3.9)$; 1 mark for correct answer.*

**Page 81, Prisms and cylinders**

**1.** $20 \times 30 \times 10 = 6000\,\text{mm}^3$
*1 mark for correct answer circled. Remember mm is a unit of length not volume.*

**2.** $25 \times 8 = 200\,\text{m}^3$
*1 mark for 200; 1 mark for $\text{m}^3$.*

**3. a** Volume $= \pi \times 4^2 \times 11 = 176\pi\,\text{cm}^3$
*1 mark for $\pi \times 4^2 \times 11$; 1 mark for $176\pi$.*

**b** Curved surface area $= 2 \times \pi \times 4 \times 11 = 88\pi$
Area of circular base $= \pi \times 4^2 = 16\pi$
Total surface area $= 88\pi + 16\pi + 16\pi$
$\qquad\qquad\qquad\quad = 120\pi$
$\qquad\qquad\qquad\quad = 376.99\ldots$
$\qquad\qquad\qquad\quad = 377\,\text{cm}^2$ to 3 sf
*1 mark for $2 \times \pi \times 4 \times 11\ (= 88\pi)$; 1 mark for $\pi \times 4^2\ (= 16\pi)$;*
*1 mark for adding all 3 surfaces ($120\pi$ or $376.99\ldots$);*
*1 mark for correct answer of 377. Total 4 marks.*

**4.** Use cm.
First prism $= \frac{1}{2} \times 1.6 \times 1.8 \times 11 = 15.84$
Second prism $= \frac{1}{2} \times 2.4 \times h \times 4 = 4.8h$
$\qquad 15.84 = 4.8h$
$\qquad\quad h = \frac{15.84}{4.8} = 3.3\,\text{cm}$
*1 mark for $\frac{1}{2} \times 1.6 \times 1.8 \times 11\ (= 15.84)$ or $\frac{1}{2} \times 2.4 \times h \times 4$*
*$(= 4.8h)$ or either without $\frac{1}{2}$; 1 mark for $15.84 = 4.8h$ or*
*$31.68 = 9.6h$; 1 mark for 3.3; 1 mark for cm. Total 4 marks.*
*Note that you could use mm as an alternative method.*

**Page 82, Spheres**

**1.** $40 \times 10^2 = 4000\,\text{mm}^2$
*1 mark for correct answer circled.*

**2.** $120 \div 100^3 = 0.000\,12\,\text{cm}^3$
*1 mark for $120 \div 100^3$ or $1\,\text{cm}^3 = 0.000\,001\,\text{m}^3$ etc.; 1 mark for correct answer.*

**3. a** Volume $= \frac{4}{3} \times \pi \times 18.2^3 = 25\,252.4\,\text{cm}^3$
**b** Surface area $= 4 \times \pi \times 18.2^2 = 4162.5\,\text{cm}^2$
*For each part, 1 mark for using correct formula; 1 mark for correct answer in terms of $\pi$.*

**4. a** Volume $= \frac{4}{3} \times \pi \times 5^3 = \frac{500}{3\pi}\,\text{cm}^3$
*1 mark for $\frac{4}{3} \times \pi \times 5^3$; 1 mark for correct answer.*
**b** Surface area $= 4 \times \pi \times 5^2 = 100\pi\,\text{cm}^2$
*1 mark for $4 \times \pi \times 5^2$; 1 mark for $100\pi$; 1 mark for $\text{cm}^2$. Total 3 marks.*

**5.** $4 \times \pi \times r^2 = 400\pi$
$\qquad\qquad\ \ r^2 = 100$
$\qquad\qquad\ \ r = 10\,\text{cm}$
*1 mark for $4 \times \pi \times r^2 = 400\pi$ or $r^2 = 100$; 1 mark for correct answer.*

**Page 83, Pyramids and cones**

**1. a** Volume $= \frac{1}{3} \times \pi \times 10^2 \times 24 = 800\pi\,\text{cm}^3$
*1 mark for $\frac{1}{3} \times \pi \times 10^2 \times 24$; 1 mark for correct answer.*
**b** Curved surface area $= \pi \times 10 \times 26 = 260\pi$
Base area $= \pi \times 10^2 = 100\pi$
Total surface area $= 260\pi + 100\pi = 360\pi\,\text{cm}^2$
*1 mark for $\pi \times 10 \times 26\ (= 260\pi)$; 1 mark for $\pi \times 10^2$*
*$(= 100\pi)$; 1 mark for correct final answer. Total 3 marks.*

**2.** Area of base $= 230 \times 230 = 52\,900$
Volume $= \frac{1}{3} \times 52\,900 \times 147 = 2\,592\,100\,\text{m}^3$
$\qquad\qquad\qquad\qquad\qquad = 2\,600\,000\,\text{m}^3$ to 2 sf
*1 mark for $230 \times 230\ (= 52\,900)$; 1 mark for*
*$\frac{1}{3} \times 52\,900 \times 147\ (= 2\,592\,100)$; 1 mark for correct answer to*
*2 sf. Total 3 marks.*

**3.** Curved surface area $= \pi \times r \times 7 = 21\pi$
$\qquad\qquad\qquad\qquad\quad 7r = 21$
$\qquad\qquad\qquad\qquad\quad\ r = 3\,\text{cm}$
Area of base $= \pi \times 3^2 = 9\pi = 28.274\ldots$
$\qquad\qquad\qquad\qquad\quad\ = 28.3\,\text{cm}^2$ to 1 dp
*1 mark for using formula for curved surface area; 1 mark for attempting to solve equation; 1 mark for correct answer. Total 3 marks.*

**Page 84, Constructing triangles**

**1. a** B
*1 mark for correct answer circled. The sum of the two sides must be more than the third side.*

**b**

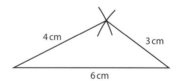

*1 mark for one side correctly drawn; 1 mark for second side; 1 mark for fully correct diagram (any orientation).*

**2.** Accurately constructed triangle
*1 mark for 6 cm line; 1 mark for either angle correctly drawn; 1 mark for fully correct diagram. Total 3 marks.*

**3.** SAS known, so use ruler and protractor.

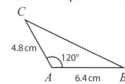

*1 mark* for 120° angle correctly drawn; *1 mark* for either 6.4 cm line or 4.8 cm line correctly drawn; *1 mark* for fully correct diagram (this includes a reflection or rotation of the one shown). Total 3 marks.

**4.** $EF = 66 \div 3 \times 2 = 44$ mm
$FD = 44 \div 4 \times 3 = 33$ mm
SSS known, so use ruler and compasses.

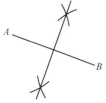

*1 mark* for each line (correct to 1 mm). Total 3 marks.

## Page 85, Perpendiculars and bisectors

**1. a**

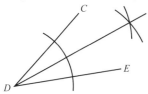

*1 mark* for intersecting construction arcs either side of line segment; *1 mark* for fully correct diagram.

**b**

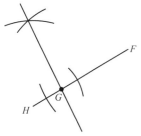

*1 mark* for construction arcs intersecting between $C$ and $E$; *1 mark* for fully correct diagram.

**2.**

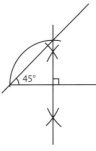

*1 mark* for construction arcs both sides of $G$; *1 mark* for second set of intersecting construction arcs either side of line segment (either above the line $FH$ as shown, or below); *1 mark* for fully correct diagram. Total 3 marks.

**3.** First, construct a right angle.

*1 mark* for construction arcs either side of a line segment and perpendicular line drawn; *1 mark* for arc intersecting perpendicular line; *1 mark* for fully correct diagram with angle labelled. Total 3 marks.
Full marks also given if instead of using the arc to make a triangle, you correctly bisected the 90° angle constructed.

## Page 86, Loci

**1.**

*1 mark* for circle with centre $P$; *1 mark* for 2 cm radius.

**2.**

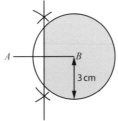

*1 mark* for construction arcs either side of $AB$ and perpendicular bisector drawn; *1 mark* for circle centre $B$; *1 mark* for 3 cm radius; *1 mark* for correctly shaded region. Total 4 marks.

**3.**

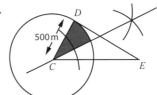

*1 mark* for pair of intersecting arcs in the space between $D$ and $E$; *1 mark* for angle bisector drawn; *1 mark* for circle or arc centre $C$ with radius of $CD$; *1 mark* for correct shaded region. Total 4 marks.

**4.**

*1 mark* for any correct straight line 2 cm from the T; *1 mark* for any semicircle in correct position; *1 mark* for fully correct locus. Total 3 marks.

## Page 87, Pythagoras' theorem

**1. D**
*1 mark* for correct answer circled. Pythagoras' theorem holds true: $7^2 + 24^2 = 25^2$

**2. a** $x^2 = 6^2 + 8^2$      **b** $y^2 = 13^2 - 12^2$
$\quad\quad x^2 = 100$ $\quad\quad\quad\quad y^2 = 25$
$\quad\quad x = 10$ cm $\quad\quad\quad\quad y = 5$ cm
For each part, *1 mark* for squaring and subtracting; *1 mark* for taking the square root of your answer; *1 mark* for correct answer. Total 3 marks.

**3. a** $x^2 = 15^2 + 11^2$      **b** $y^2 = 34^2 - 29^2$
$\quad\quad x^2 = 346$ $\quad\quad\quad\quad y^2 = 315$
$\quad\quad x = 18.6$ cm to 1 dp $\quad\quad y = 17.7$ cm to 1 dp
For each part, *1 mark* for squaring and subtracting; *1 mark* for taking the square root of your answer; *1 mark* for correct rounded answer. Total 3 marks.

**4.**

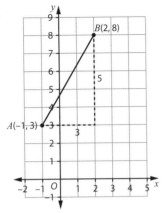

From the diagram,
$(AB)^2 = 5^2 + 3^2 = 34$
$AB = 5.83\ldots = 5.83\,\text{cm (3 sf)}$
*1 mark for identifying at least one of 3 and 5 as sides of a right-angled triangle; **1 mark** for squaring and adding; **1 mark** for taking the square root of your answer; **1 mark** for correct answer to 3 sf. Total 4 marks.*

**5.**

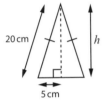

From the diagram,
$h^2 = 20^2 - 5^2 = 375$
$h = 19.364\ldots = 19.4\,\text{cm (1 dp)}$
*1 mark for splitting into two right-angled triangles with side 5; **1 mark** for squaring and subtracting; **1 mark** for correct answer to 1 dp. Total 3 marks.*

## Page 88, Trigonometry 1

**1. a** $x = 16\cos 35° = 13.1\,\text{cm to 1 dp}$
   **b** $y = 42\tan 27° = 21.4\,\text{cm to 1 dp}$
   **c** $z = \dfrac{14}{\sin 67°} = 15.2\,\text{cm to 1 dp}$
   **d** $p = 6\sin 32° = 3.2\,\text{cm to 1 dp}$
   **e** $q = \dfrac{10}{\tan 47°} = 9.3\,\text{cm to 1 dp}$
   **f** $r = \dfrac{8}{\cos 62°} = 17.0\,\text{cm to 1 dp}$
   *For each part, **1 mark** for correct calculation; **1 mark** for correct answer to 1 dp.*

**2.** The trapezium can be split into a rectangle 24 cm by $h$ cm and a right-angled triangle of height $h$.
   Base of triangle = 40 – 24 = 16 cm
   $h = 16\tan 50° = 19.1\,\text{cm to 3 sf}$
   *1 mark for 40 – 24 (= 16); **1 mark** for 16 tan 50°; **1 mark** for correct answer to 3 sf. Total 3 marks.*

**3.** Distance = $\dfrac{1000}{\sin 26°} = 2281.17\ldots = 2300\,\text{m to 2 sf}$
   *1 mark for $\dfrac{1000}{\sin 26°}$; **1 mark** for correct answer to 2 sf.*

## Page 89, Trigonometry 2

**1.** $\dfrac{9}{15}$
   *1 mark for correct answer circled. Remember sin of the angle you want is opposite side over hypotenuse.*

**2. a** $\sin x = \dfrac{4}{7}$
   $x = \sin^{-1}\left(\dfrac{4}{7}\right) = 34.8°\,\text{to 1 dp}$

   **b** $\tan x = \dfrac{10}{11}$
   $x = \tan^{-1}\left(\dfrac{10}{11}\right) = 42.3°\,\text{to 1 dp}$
   **c** $\cos x = \dfrac{13}{20}$
   $x = \cos^{-1}\left(\dfrac{13}{20}\right) = 49.5°\,\text{to 1 dp}$
   *For each part, **1 mark** for correct calculation; **1 mark** for correct answer to 1 dp.*

**3.**

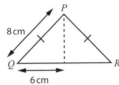

$\cos PQR = \dfrac{6}{8}$
$PQR = \cos^{-1}\left(\dfrac{6}{8}\right) = 41.4°\,\text{to 1 dp}$
*1 mark for 12 ÷ 2 (= 6); **1 mark** for $\cos PQR = \dfrac{6}{8}$, **1 mark** for correct answer to 1 dp. Total 3 marks.*

**4.**

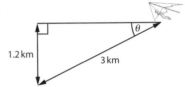

Let the required angle be $\theta$.
$\sin\theta = \dfrac{1.2}{3}$
$\theta = \sin^{-1}\left(\dfrac{1.2}{3}\right) = 23.6°\,\text{to 3 sf}$
*1 mark for identifying the correct angle (could be on the diagram or could be implied by a correct calculation); **1 mark** for $\sin\theta = \dfrac{1.2}{3}$, **1 mark** for correct answer to 3 sf. Total 3 marks.*

## Page 90, Exact values

**1.** 1
   *1 mark for correct answer circled. Remember sin 0° = 0*

**2. a** $x = 4\sin 30° = 4 \times \dfrac{1}{2} = 2\,\text{cm}$
   *1 mark for 4 sin 30°; **1 mark** for sin 30° = $\dfrac{1}{2}$; **1 mark** for correct final answer. Total 3 marks.*
   **b** $x = 1 \times \tan 45° = 1 \times 1 = 1\,\text{cm}$
   *1 mark for 1 × tan 45°; **1 mark** for tan 45° = 1; **1 mark** for correct final answer. Total 3 marks.*
   **c** $x = \dfrac{6}{\cos 60°} = \dfrac{6}{\frac{1}{2}} = 12\,\text{cm}$
   *1 mark for $\dfrac{6}{\cos 60°}$; **1 mark** for cos 60° = $\dfrac{1}{2}$; **1 mark** for correct final answer. Total 3 marks.*

**3. a** $\dfrac{1}{\sqrt{2}}$
   *1 mark for $\dfrac{1}{\sqrt{2}}$ or $\dfrac{\sqrt{2}}{2}$*
   **b** $1 + \dfrac{1}{2} = 1\dfrac{1}{2}$
   *1 mark for either 1 or $\dfrac{1}{2}$; **1 mark** for correct answer (or equivalent e.g. $\dfrac{3}{2}$, 1.5).*
   **c** $\dfrac{\sqrt{3}}{2}$
   *1 mark for correct answer.*
   **d** $\sqrt{3} - 0 = \sqrt{3}$
   *1 mark for either $\sqrt{3}$ or 0; **1 mark** for correct answer.*

**4 a**

| | 0° | 30° | 45° | 60° | 90° |
|---|---|---|---|---|---|
| sin | 0 | $\frac{1}{2}$ | $\frac{1}{\sqrt{2}}$ | $\frac{\sqrt{3}}{2}$ | ⓪ |
| cos | 1 | $\frac{\sqrt{3}}{2}$ | ⓪$\frac{\sqrt{3}}{2}$ | $\frac{1}{2}$ | 0 |
| tan | 0 | ⓪$\sqrt{3}$ | 1 | ⓪$\frac{\sqrt{3}}{2}$ | undefined |

*1 mark for each correct answer circled. (Note: 1 mark deducted for each incorrect answer circled.) Total 4 marks.*

**b**  $\sin 90° = 1$

$\cos 45° = \frac{1}{\sqrt{2}}$ or $\frac{\sqrt{2}}{2}$

$\tan 30° = \frac{1}{\sqrt{3}}$ or $\frac{\sqrt{3}}{3}$

$\tan 60° = \sqrt{3}$

*1 mark for each correct answer. Total 4 marks.*

## Page 91, Vectors

**1.** 3**a**

*1 mark for correct answer.*

**2.** –**b**

*1 mark for any answer of the form –k**b**, where k is a positive number.*

**3. a**  $\overrightarrow{PO} = -\mathbf{p}$

*1 mark for correct answer.*

**b**  $\overrightarrow{PQ} = \overrightarrow{OR} = \mathbf{r}$

$\overrightarrow{OP} + \overrightarrow{PQ} = \mathbf{p} + \mathbf{r}$

*1 mark for correct answer (also accept **r** + **p**).*

**c**  $\overrightarrow{QO} = \overrightarrow{QP} + \overrightarrow{PO} = -\mathbf{r} - \mathbf{p}$

*1 mark for correct answer (also accept –**p** – **r**).*

**4.** Parallelogram

*1 mark for correct answer circled (not a square since it's regular).*

**5. a**  $\overrightarrow{OT} = \overrightarrow{QO} = -3\mathbf{b}$

*1 mark for correct answer.*

**b**  $\overrightarrow{PQ} = \overrightarrow{PO} + \overrightarrow{OQ} = -2\mathbf{a} + 3\mathbf{b}$

*1 mark for correct answer (also accept 3**b** –2**a**).*

**c**  $\overrightarrow{OU} = \overrightarrow{OP} + \overrightarrow{PU} = 2\mathbf{a} - 3\mathbf{b}$

*1 mark for correct answer (also accept –3**b** +2**a**).*

**d**  $\overrightarrow{UQ} = \overrightarrow{UP} + \overrightarrow{PQ} = 3\mathbf{b} -2\mathbf{a} + 3\mathbf{b} = 6\mathbf{b} - 2\mathbf{a}$

*1 mark for $\overrightarrow{UP} + \overrightarrow{PQ}$; 1 mark for correct answer (also accept –2**a** +6**b**).*

## Page 92, Column vectors

**1. a**  $4\begin{pmatrix} -2 \\ 3 \end{pmatrix} = \begin{pmatrix} -8 \\ 12 \end{pmatrix}$

*1 mark for correct answer.*

**b**  $\begin{pmatrix} -2 \\ 3 \end{pmatrix} + \begin{pmatrix} -1 \\ 4 \end{pmatrix} = \begin{pmatrix} -3 \\ 7 \end{pmatrix}$

*1 mark for correct answer.*

**c**  $2\begin{pmatrix} -1 \\ 4 \end{pmatrix} - 3\begin{pmatrix} -2 \\ 3 \end{pmatrix} = \begin{pmatrix} -2 \\ 8 \end{pmatrix} - \begin{pmatrix} -6 \\ 9 \end{pmatrix} = \begin{pmatrix} 4 \\ -1 \end{pmatrix}$

*1 mark for either $\begin{pmatrix} -2 \\ 8 \end{pmatrix}$ or $\begin{pmatrix} -6 \\ 9 \end{pmatrix}$; 1 mark for correct answer.*

**2.** $\begin{pmatrix} -2x \\ 6 \end{pmatrix} = \begin{pmatrix} y \\ x \end{pmatrix}$

$x = 6$ and $y = -12$

*1 mark for correct x; 1 mark for correct y.*

**3.** $\mathbf{f} = \begin{pmatrix} -1 \\ 4 \end{pmatrix}$, $\mathbf{g} = \begin{pmatrix} 5 \\ 0 \end{pmatrix}$, $\mathbf{h} = \begin{pmatrix} 3 \\ -2 \end{pmatrix}$

*1 mark for each correct vector. Total 3 marks.*

**4.**

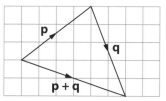

*1 mark for each of vectors **p** and **q** drawn correctly (with arrows in correct directions); 1 mark for creating a triangle with your **p** and **q** (with arrow in correct direction); 1 mark for fully correct diagram. Total 4 marks.*

**5.**

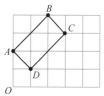

$\overrightarrow{PQ} = \begin{pmatrix} 3 \\ 3 \end{pmatrix}$

*1 mark for identifying the location of C; 1 mark for correct column vector.*

## Page 93, Sampling

**1. a**  Quantitative secondary data

*1 mark for quantitative; 1 mark for secondary.*

**b**  Data not current, out-of-date etc.

*1 mark for suitable reason.*

**2. a**  Convenient, cheap   **b**  Unreliable

*1 mark for each correct answer.*

**3. a**  $8 \div 40 \times 180 = 36$

*1 mark for $8 \div 40 \times 180$ or $180 \div 5$; 1 mark for correct answer.*

**b**  Representative sample, random sample, no bias etc.

*1 mark for suitable reason.*

**4. a**  Every item has an equal chance of selection.

*1 mark for any correct answer.*

**b i**   All pupils at the school

**ii**   The five friends who were chosen

*1 mark for each correct answer.*

**c**  Not every pupil had an equal chance of selection, so the sample isn't random.

*1 mark for correct answer.*

**d**  Take a larger sample; use a random method of selection.

*1 mark for one correct answer; 1 mark for second correct answer.*

## Page 94, Organising data

**1. a**  Median = 2.1   **b**  Mode = 2.8

*1 mark for each correct answer.*

**2.** From top to bottom: 5, 6, 2, 5, 2

*1 mark for no more than 1 error; 1 mark for fully correct.*

**3. a**

| | Tea | Coffee | Total |
|---|---|---|---|
| **Sugar** | **6** | 5 | **11** |
| **No sugar** | 3 | 7 | 10 |
| **Total** | 9 | **12** | 21 |

*1 mark for any two values correct; 1 mark for fully correct table.*

**b**  10

*1 mark for correct answer.*

**4.** Physics: Median = (68 + 71) ÷ 2 = 69.5
    Range = 74 − 50 = 24
Maths:  Median = (64 + 67) ÷ 2 = 65.5
    Range = 79 − 52 = 27
Physics scores are higher on average.
There is more variation in the Maths scores.
*1 mark any two correct calculations (for median or range);*
*1 mark if all calculations correct; 1 mark for correct*
*statement comparing medians; 1 mark for correct*
*statement comparing ranges. Total 4 marks.*

## Page 95, Simple charts

**1. a** 4
    *1 mark for correct answer.*
**b** 42
    *1 mark for correct answer.*
**c**

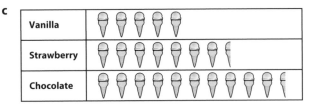

*1 mark for 5 ice cream cones drawn for vanilla.*

**2.**

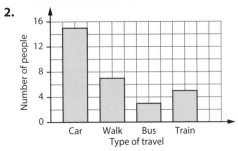

*1 mark for any linear scale on vertical axis (goes up in equal*
*amounts per square) and both axes labelled; 1 mark for at*
*least one bar drawn with correct height; 1 mark for fully*
*correct. Total 3 marks.*

**3. a** 20
    *1 mark for correct answer.*
**b** 50 − 30 = 20
    *1 mark for correct answer.*
**c**

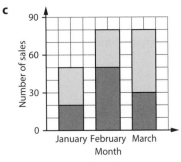

*1 mark for correct height of bar for March for either*
*shoes or socks; 1 mark for fully correct composite bar*
*for March.*

## Page 96, Pie charts

**1.** 200 ÷ 4 = 50 people
    *1 mark for correct answer circled.*

**2.**

| Favourite type | Science fiction | Fantasy | Romance | Other | Total |
|---|---|---|---|---|---|
| Frequency | 34 | 20 | 6 | 12 | **72** |
| Angle | **170°** | 100° | **30°** | **60°** | 360° |

*1 mark for table fully correct; 1 mark for any correct angle*
*correctly measured; 1 mark for fully correct and labelled pie*
*chart. Total 3 marks.*

**3.** No, as there might be fewer pupils at Summerton High.
    *1 mark for any comment comparing the numbers of*
    *students at each school; 1 mark for 'No' with clear*
    *explanation. (Accept comments such as 'not necessarily'*
    *or 'maybe' etc. as long as they are supported by a clear*
    *justification comparing the number of pupils at each*
    *school.)*

## Page 97, Averages and spread

**1.** In order, you have 28 30 31 32 34 37 39
    Therefore, the median is 32
    *1 mark for correct answer.*
**2. a** 2
    *1 mark for correct answer.*
**b** In order, you have 1 1 2 2 2 2 2 3 4 4 6 6 6 7 8 8
    Therefore, the median = (3 + 4) ÷ 2 = 3.5
    *1 mark for writing the numbers in order (could be largest*
    *to smallest) or for (3 + 4) ÷ 2; 1 mark for correct answer.*
**c** The sum of the numbers is 64
    Therefore, the mean = 64 ÷ 16 = 4
    *1 mark for adding all of the numbers and dividing by 16;*
    *1 mark for correct answer.*
**d** 8 − 1 = 7
    *1 mark for correct answer.*
**3. a** Mode, since data is non-numerical.
    **b** Median, since data contains extreme values or outliers.
    **c** Mean, since no extreme values/outliers.
    *For each part, 1 mark for correct average; 1 mark for*
    *correct reason.*
**4.** The answer is 2 6 8 8
    There are 4 numbers and the mean is 6, so the total of the
    numbers is 4 × 6 = 24
    The mode is 8, so there must be at least two 8s.
    There cannot be three 8s as then the total would be more
    than 24. Therefore, the only 8s are the 3rd and 4th numbers.
    If the median is 7, then the 2nd number must be 6. For
    the total to be 24, the remaining number must be 2
    *1 mark for any 4 numbers with a total of 24 or with a mode*
    *of 8 or with a median of 7; 1 mark for fully correct answer.*
**5.** 63 × 10 = 630 (total of all 10 numbers)
    51 × 4 = 204 (total of 4 of the numbers)
    630 − 204 = 426 (total of remaining 6 numbers)

The mean of the remaining 6 numbers is 426 ÷ 6 = 71
*1 mark for 630 or 204; 1 mark for subtracting your 204 from your 630 and dividing by 6; 1 mark for correct answer of 71. Total 3 marks.*

## Page 98, Averages from tables

**1. a**

| Score on dice | Tally | Frequency |
|---|---|---|
| 1 | IIII | 4 |
| 2 | II | 2 |
| 3 | ⊪ I | 6 |
| 4 | II | 2 |
| 5 | III | 3 |
| 6 | III | 3 |

*1 mark for at most 2 errors; 1 mark for fully correct table.*

**b i** 3      **ii** 6 – 1 = 5

**iii** Value half way between 10th and 11th value = 3
*1 mark for each correct answer.*

**2. a**

| Number of goals, $g$ | Frequency, $f$ | $g \times f$ |
|---|---|---|
| 0 | 5 | 0 |
| 1 | 6 | 6 |
| 2 | 5 | 10 |
| 3 | 4 | 12 |
| Total | 20 | 28 |

Mean = 28 ÷ 20 = 1.4
*1 mark for attempt to multiply number of goals by frequency (i.e. any correct value in the final column); 1 mark for either total correct (20 or 28) or for dividing your column 3 total by your column 2 total; 1 mark for correct answer. Total 3 marks.*

**b i** Highest number of goals scored is 2
Lowest number of goals scored is 1
Range = 2 – 1 = 1
*1 mark for correct answer circled.*

**ii** Mean for Fermat United is 1.4
Mean for Gauss Town is 1.4
They score the same number of goals per match on average.
*1 mark for comparing means; 1 mark for comparing means with correct conclusion.*

**iii** Range for Fermat United is 1
Range for Gauss Town is 3 – 0 = 3
Fermat United have the lower range and so are more consistent
*1 mark for comparing your ranges or for stating that the range for Gauss Town = 3; 1 mark for comparing ranges with correct conclusion.*

## Page 99, Grouped data

**1. a**

| Length ($x$ cm) | Frequency, $f$ | Midpoint | $f \times$ midpoint |
|---|---|---|---|
| $0 < x \le 8$ | 50 | 4 | 200 |
| $8 < x \le 16$ | 30 | 12 | **360** |
| $16 < x \le 24$ | 20 | **20** | 400 |
| Total | 100 | | **960** |

*1 mark for 20 or 360 or 960; 1 mark for fully correct table.*

**b** $0 < x \le 8$
*1 mark for correct answer.*

**c** Estimated mean length = 960 ÷ 100 = 9.6 cm
*1 mark for dividing the final column total by 100; 1 mark for 9.6 cm.*

**2. a** $\frac{71 + 1}{2} = 36$
The median is the 36th value.
Median class = $30 < t \le 35$
*1 mark for $\frac{71+1}{2}$ (= 36); 1 mark for $30 < t \le 35$*

**b**

| Time ($t$ minutes) | Frequency | Midpoint | Frequency × midpoint |
|---|---|---|---|
| $20 < t \le 25$ | 10 | **22.5** | **225** |
| $25 < t \le 30$ | 17 | **27.5** | **467.5** |
| $30 < t \le 35$ | 24 | **32.5** | **780** |
| $35 < t \le 40$ | 11 | **37.5** | **412.5** |
| $40 < t \le 45$ | 9 | **42.5** | **382.5** |
| | **71** | | **2267.5** |

Estimate for mean = 2267.5 ÷ 71 = 31.93…
This is 32 minutes to the nearest minute.
*1 mark for multiplying frequencies by your midpoints; 1 mark for dividing your final column total by 71 or for 31.93…; 1 mark for correct answer to nearest minute. Total 3 marks.*

**c** You don't know the actual data values, so you can only provide an estimate by using midpoints.
*1 mark for clear explanation.*

**3.**

| Score ($x$) | Frequency | Midpoint | Frequency × midpoint |
|---|---|---|---|
| $0 < t \le 4$ | $3y$ | **2** | **$6y$** |
| $4 < t \le 8$ | $7y$ | **6** | **$42y$** |
| | **$10y$** | | **$48y$** |

Estimate for mean = $48y ÷ 10y = 4.8$
*1 mark for multiplying frequencies by your midpoints; 1 mark for dividing your final column total by your frequency total; 1 mark for correct answer of 4.8. (Note that if calculations do not contain $y$, then full marks can still be awarded for this question.) Total 3 marks.*

## Page 100, Scatter graphs

**1. a** None    **b** Negative    **c** Positive
*1 mark for each correct answer.*

**2. a**

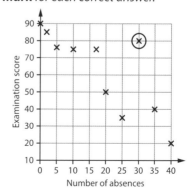

*1 mark for at most one error in points plotted; 1 mark if all correct.*

**b** Outlier at (30, 80) circled on graph (see above)
*1 mark* for correct answer.

**c** Negative
*1 mark* for correct answer.

**3. a** Positive      **b** (75, 2)
*1 mark* for each correct answer.

## Page 101, Lines of best fit

**1. a**

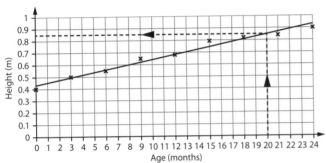

*1 mark* for line of best fit drawn as above.

**b** 0.85 m (see graph)
*1 mark* for a value between 0.83 and 0.87

**c** Outside of range of data values (extrapolation)
*1 mark* for suitable explanation.

**2.** Both are affected by warm weather but not by each other.
*1 mark* for suitable explanation.

**3. a**

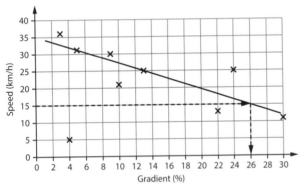

*1 mark* for line of best fit drawn as above.

**b** 26% (see graph)
*1 mark* for a value between 24 and 28

**c** Unreliable as outside range of data values (extrapolation)
*1 mark* for suitable explanation.

## Page 102, Time series

**1.** Decreasing
*1 mark* for correct answer.

**2. a**

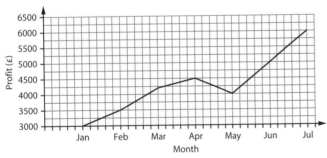

*1 mark* for any 6 points correctly plotted and joined with straight lines; *1 mark* for all points correctly plotted.

**b** Increasing
*1 mark* for correct answer.

**c** The scale on the $y$-axis starts at 3000/does not start at 0
*1 mark* for correct answer.

**3. a** Decreasing
*1 mark* for correct answer.

**b** Week 1 and Week 4
*1 mark* for both correct.

**c** Approximately 150
*1 mark* for anything between 100 and 200

## Page 103, Theoretical probability

**1. a** $\frac{1}{6}$     **b** $\frac{3}{6}$ or $\frac{1}{2}$     **c** $\frac{2}{6}$ or $\frac{1}{3}$
*1 mark* for each correct answer.

**2. a** A     **b** C     **c** B
*1 mark* for each correct answer.

**3.** $\frac{2}{3}$
*1 mark* for correct answer circled.

**4. a** Letter A     **b** $\frac{4}{5}$ or 0.8
*1 mark* for each correct answer.

**5.** $x + x + \frac{1}{2} = 1$
$$2x = \frac{1}{2}$$
$$x = \frac{1}{4}$$
*1 mark* for $x + x + \frac{1}{2} = 1$ or $2x = \frac{1}{2}$; *1 mark* for correct answer of $\frac{1}{4}$ or 0.25

## Page 104, Mutually exclusive events

**1. a** Yes     **b** No     **c** Yes
*1 mark* for each correct answer.

**2.** $1 - 0.1 = 0.9$
*1 mark* for correct answer.

**3. a** $\frac{1}{50}$ or 0.02
*1 mark* for correct answer.

**b** Multiples of 8 are:
8, 16, 24, 32, 40, 48 (6 numbers)
P(multiple of 8) $= \frac{6}{50}$
P(not a multiple of 8) $= 1 - \frac{6}{50} = \frac{44}{50}$
*1 mark* for $\frac{6}{50}$ or for 1 – your P(multiple of 8) or for 44;
*1 mark* for correct answer of $\frac{44}{50}$ (or equivalent e.g. $\frac{22}{25}$, 0.88).

**c** Possible numbers are:
3, 13, 23, 30 to 39, 43 (14 numbers)
P(contains at least one 3) $= \frac{14}{50}$
*1 mark* for 14 or for listing all possibilities (allow 1 error or omission); *1 mark* for correct answer of $\frac{14}{50}$ (or equivalent e.g. $\frac{7}{25}$, 0.28).

**4. a** $1 - (0.3 + 0.15 + 0.26) = 1 - 0.71 = 0.29$
*1 mark* for $1 - (0.3 + 0.15 + 0.26)$ or $1 - 0.71$; *1 mark* for correct answer of 0.29 or $\frac{29}{100}$

**b** P(not white or pink)
$= $ P(yellow or orange) $= 0.15 + 0.29 = 0.44$
*1 mark* for $0.15 + 0.29$; *1 mark* for correct answer of $0.44, \frac{44}{100}, \frac{22}{50}$ or $\frac{11}{25}$
Note that there are alternative methods.

**c** P(yellow) $= 0.15$
$0.15 \times 200 = 30$
*1 mark* for $0.15 \times 200$; *1 mark* for correct answer of 30
Note that there are alternative methods.

## Page 105, Possibility spaces

**1. a** $\frac{1}{36}$  **b** $\frac{10}{36}$ or $\frac{5}{18}$  **c** $\frac{18}{36}$ or equivalent e.g. $\frac{1}{2}$

*1 mark for each correct answer.*

**2. a**

| + | 1 | 2 | 3 | 4 |
|---|---|---|---|---|
| **1** | 2 | 3 | 4 | 5 |
| **2** | 3 | 4 | 5 | 6 |
| **3** | 4 | 5 | 6 | 7 |
| **4** | 5 | 6 | 7 | 8 |

*1 mark for no more than 2 errors; 1 mark for all correct.*

**b** $\frac{3}{16}$

*1 mark for correct answer.*

**c** Jacob should choose 5 as it appears most often in the sample space.

*1 mark for stating that Jacob should choose 5; 1 mark for justification e.g. highest probability (= $\frac{4}{16} = \frac{1}{4}$).*

**3. a** WWW, WWL, WLL, LLL

*1 mark for 2 correct outcomes; 1 mark for all correct.*

**b** $\frac{3}{4}$ or 75%

*2 marks for correct answer.*

## Page 106, Probability experiments

**1. a**

| | Pin up | Pin down |
|---|---|---|
| **Frequency** | 35 | **15** |
| **Relative frequency** | **0.7** | 0.3 |

*1 mark for 15; 1 mark for 0.7*

**b** $\frac{40}{100}$ or equivalent e.g. $\frac{4}{10}$, $\frac{2}{5}$, 0.4

*1 mark for correct answer.*

**2.** $0.2 = \frac{2}{10} = \frac{4}{20}$

The coin was thrown 20 times.

*1 mark for $\frac{4}{20}$, 1 mark for final answer of 20*

**3. a**

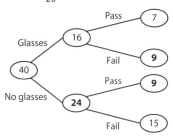

*1 mark for no more than 1 error; 1 mark for fully correct.*

**b** $\frac{7}{40}$

*1 mark for correct answer.*

**4. a**

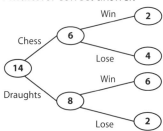

*1 mark for no more than 2 errors; 1 mark for fully correct.*

**b** $\frac{4}{14}$ or $\frac{2}{7}$

*1 mark for correct answer.*

## Page 107, Expected results

**1.** $0.3 \times 20 = 6$

Expect the bus to be late 6 times.

*1 mark for correct answer circled.*

**2.** $20 + 16 + 24 + 20 = 80$ sweets

**a** P(red) = $\frac{24}{80}$

*1 mark for correct answer or equivalent e.g. $\frac{3}{10}$, 0.3*

**b** $\frac{24}{80} = \frac{6}{20}$

Expect 6 to be red.

*1 mark for $\frac{6}{20}$ or $\frac{24}{80} \times 20$; 1 mark for correct answer of 6*

**3. a** $0.85 \times 60 = 51$

Expect 51 reports on time.

*1 mark for $0.85 \times 60$ or $\frac{51}{60}$; 1 mark for correct answer.*

**b** $0.85 \times 170 = 144.5$

$160 > 144.5$, so more than expected.

*1 mark for $0.85 \times 170$; 1 mark for correct answer.*

*Note that there are alternative methods.*

**4. a** $\frac{3}{8}$ or 0.375

*1 mark for correct answer.*

**b** $\frac{2}{8} \times 40 = 10$

Expect it 10 times.

*1 mark for $\frac{2}{8} \times 40$ or $\frac{10}{40}$; 1 mark for correct answer.*

**c** $36 \div 3 \times 8 = 96$

Expect 96 rolls.

*1 mark for $36 \div 3 \times 8$ or $\frac{36}{96}$; 1 mark for correct answer.*

**5.** P(lands on 5) = $1 - (0.2 + 0.4 + 0.16 + 0.13) = 0.11$

$2500 \times 0.11 = 275$

Expect 275 times.

*1 mark for $1 - (0.2 + 0.4 + 0.16 + 0.13)$ or 0.11; 1 mark for $2500 \times$ your probability of the spinner landing on 5; 1 mark for correct answer. Total 3 marks.*

## Page 108, Tree diagrams

**1.** $0.4 \times 0.5 = 0.2$

*1 mark for correct answer circled.*

**2. a**

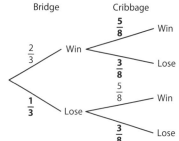

*1 mark for any correct probability; 1 mark for fully correct.*

**b** $\frac{2}{3} \times \frac{5}{8} = \frac{10}{24}$

*1 mark for $\frac{2}{3} \times \frac{5}{8}$; 1 mark for correct answer or equivalent e.g. $\frac{5}{12}$*

**3.** Regardless of whether Chen gets the first question correct or incorrect, the probability of getting the second question correct is $\frac{1}{4}$

*1 mark for correct answer of $\frac{1}{4}$*

*Note that there are alternative methods.*

# Page 109, Set notation

**1.**

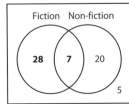

*1 mark* for 28 in correct position; *1 mark* for 7 in correct position.

**2.**

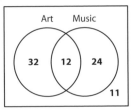

*1 mark* for each number placed in correct position. Total 4 marks.

**3. a** {2, 3, 6, 7, 9, 10, 12}   **b** {10, 12, 17, 18}

*1 mark* for each correct answer.

**4. a**

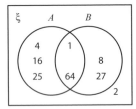

*1 mark* for 4, 16 and 25 correctly placed; *1 mark* for 1 and 64 correctly placed; *1 mark* for 8 and 27 correctly placed; *1 mark* for 2 correctly placed. Total 4 marks.

**b** {1, 64}

*1 mark* for fully correct.

# Page 110, Probability from tables & diagrams

**1. a**

|        | Black | White | Total |
|--------|-------|-------|-------|
| Circle | 3     | 3     | 6     |
| Square | 3     | 1     | 4     |
| Total  | 6     | 4     | 10    |

*1 mark* for any 1 row or column correct; *1 mark* for any 2 rows or columns correct; *1 mark* if fully correct table. Total 3 marks.

**b** $\frac{3}{10}$ or 0.3

*1 mark* for correct answer.

**2. a**

|         | Good | Average | Total |
|---------|------|---------|-------|
| Snooker | 4    | 10      | 14    |
| Darts   | 8    | 13      | 21    |
| Total   | 12   | 23      | 35    |

*1 mark* for at least 3 values correct; *1 mark* for at least 5 values correct; *1 mark* for at least 7 values correct; *1 mark* if fully correct table. Total 4 marks.

**b** $\frac{4}{35}$

*1 mark* for correct answer.

**3. a**

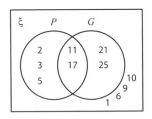

*1 mark* for 2, 3 and 5 correctly placed; *1 mark* for 11 and 17 correctly placed; *1 mark* for 21 and 25 correctly placed; *1 mark* for 1, 6, 9 and 10 correctly placed. Total 4 marks.

**b i** $\frac{2}{11}$   **ii** $\frac{7}{11}$   **iii** $\frac{3}{11}$

*1 mark* for each correct answer.

## Practice exam paper guided answers

*For further practice and support, see the page reference after each guided answer.*

### Paper 1 Non-calculator

**1.** 0.5

*1 mark* for correct answer circled.

**See page 1, Place value**

**2.** 270

*1 mark* for correct answer circled.

**See page 3, Rounding and truncating**

**3.** 30%

*1 mark* for correct answer circled.

**See page 13, Fractions, decimals, percentages**

**4.** 2

*1 mark* for correct answer circled.

**See page 11, Calculating with fractions 1**

**5. a i** $f - 6$

  **ii** $2d$

*1 mark* for each correct answer.

**b** $T = 2 \times 4 - 3 = 5$

*1 mark* for $2 \times 4 - 3$ or $8 - 3$; *1 mark* for correct answer of 5

**See page 21, Terms and expressions**

**6.** Using decimals, $\frac{7}{10} = 0.7$ and $\frac{3}{4} = 0.75$

$0.7 < 0.75$, so Constance is not correct.

*1 mark* for at least one of 0.7 or 0.75 correct; *1 mark* for fully justified and correct conclusion.

Alternatively, using fractions, $\frac{7}{10} = \frac{14}{20}$ and $\frac{3}{4} = \frac{15}{20}$, $\frac{14}{20} < \frac{15}{20}$, so Constance is not correct.

**See page 9, Introduction to Fractions and page 13, Fractions, decimals, percentages**

**7.** Total number of phone symbols Monday to Thursday

$= 4\frac{1}{2} + 3 + 4 + 5\frac{3}{4} = 17\frac{1}{4}$

Each symbol is 20 minutes so 3 represent 1 hour.

Total Monday to Friday = 7 hours 45 minutes

This is represented by $7 \times 3 + 2 + \frac{1}{4} = 23\frac{1}{4}$ symbols.

Symbols for Friday = $23\frac{1}{4} - 17\frac{1}{4} = 6$ symbols.

*1 mark* for Monday to Thursday total; *1 mark* for converting time to symbols or total symbols to time and subtracting; *1 mark* for 6 complete phones drawn next to Friday. Total 3 marks.

**See page 95, Simple charts**

**8.** $\frac{2}{3} \times 180 = 120\,g$

*1 mark* for $\frac{2}{3} \times 180$; *1 mark* for correct answer.

**See page 10, Proportion of amounts**

**9.** 1

*1 mark for correct answer circled.*

*See page 15, Calculating with indices*

**10. a**
```
    32
×   36
─────
   960
   192
─────
  1152
```
$32 \times 36 = 1152$
$3.2 \times 3.6 = 11.52$

*1 mark for any correct method used with at most 1 error; 1 mark for digits 1152; 1 mark for correct answer. Total 3 marks.*

**b** $42 \div 0.07 = 420 \div 7 = 60$

*1 mark for attempt to multiply both numbers to simplify the calculation; 1 mark for correct answer.*

*See page 8, Calculating with decimals*

**11. a** $x = 70°$

Corresponding angles (are equal.)

*1 mark for 70°; 1 mark for correct reason.*

**b** 4th angle in quadrilateral = $180° - 50° = 130°$

(Angles on a straight line sum to 180°.)

$y = 360° - 125° - 45° - 130° = 60°$

(Angles in a quadrilateral sum to 360°.)

*1 mark for 180 − 50; 1 mark for 360 − other 3 angles; 1 mark for correct answer of 60. Total 3 marks.*

*See page 63, Angle rules*

**12. a** You need to do $4 \times 5$ first.

$3 + 4 \times 5 = 3 + 20 = 23$

*1 mark for any correct explanation.*

**b** $2 + 4 \times 6^2 = 2 + 4 \times 36 = 2 + 144 = 146$

*1 mark for 36; 1 mark for correct answer.*

*See page 2, Order of operations*

**13.** $\frac{24}{30} = \frac{4}{5} = 80\%$; $\frac{21}{25} = 84\%$

84% > 80%, so sight-reading is the better score.

*1 mark each for converting to fractions with common denominator or percentages; 1 mark for correct conclusion. Total 3 marks.*

*See page 50, Proportion*

**14. a** $14\,352 \div 10 \div 10 = 143.52$

**b** $14\,352 \div 100 \times 1000 = 143\,520$

**c** $14\,352 \div 276 = 52$

$14.352 \div 0.276 = 52 \div 1000 \times 1000 = 52$

*1 mark for each correct answer.*

*See page 1, Place value*

**15. a** $360 = 6 \times 6 \times 10 = 2 \times 3 \times 2 \times 3 \times 2 \times 5$

$= 2^3 \times 3^2 \times 5$

*1 mark for attempting prime factor decomposition; 1 mark for correct answer (any order).*

**b** $15 = 5 \times 3$ and 5 and 3 are factors of 360, so 360 is divisible by 15. Rosie is correct.

*1 mark for explanation.*

*See page 17, Prime factor decomposition*

**16.** Jenny pays $12 \times 3.99 = 12 \times 4 - 0.12 = £47.88$

Zain pays £42

Zain gets the magazine cheaper.

*1 mark for 12 × 3.99; 1 mark for 47.88; 1 mark for comparison with 42 and correct conclusion that Zain gets the magazine cheaper. Total 3 marks.*

*See page 8, Calculating with decimals*

**17.** $25 - 5 = 20$ blue and yellow pencils

Number of 'parts' for blue and yellow = $3 + 1 = 4$

1 part = $20 \div 4 = 5$

There are 5 yellow and $3 \times 5 = 15$ blue pencils.

Red : blue : yellow = $5 : 15 : 5 = 1 : 3 : 1$

*1 mark for attempting to split 20 pencils into number of blue and yellow; 1 mark for 5 : 15 : 5 in any order; 1 mark for correct answer in simplest form and correct order. Total 3 marks.*

*See page 51, Ratio*

**18. a**

Pattern 4

*1 mark for correct pattern drawn.*

**b i** 15

*1 mark for correct answer circled.*

**ii** $2n + 1$

*1 mark for 2n; 1 mark for fully correct answer.*

**c** $2 \times 100 + 1 = 201$, so Darren is correct.

*1 mark for correct explanation.*

*See page 46, Sequences*

**19. a** $\frac{10 \times 100}{0.5} = \frac{1000}{0.5} = 2000$

*1 mark for 0.5 or for 10 and 100; 1 mark for fully correct including working.*

**b** It is an underestimate since numbers in numerator are rounded down and number in denominator is rounded up.

*1 mark for correct answer with explanation.*

*See page 5, Estimation*

**20.** $3(2x - 3) = 39$; $6x - 9 = 39$; $6x = 48$; $x = 8$

*1 mark for a correct algebraic step e.g. expanding brackets or dividing by 3; 1 mark for correct answer.*

*See page 27, Harder linear equations*

**21.** $1 - \frac{3}{8} = \frac{5}{8}$

$\frac{1}{2} \times \frac{5}{8} = \frac{5}{16}$

$\frac{5}{16} + \frac{3}{8} = \frac{5 + 6}{16} = \frac{11}{16}$

*1 mark for $\frac{1}{2} \times \frac{5}{8}$; 1 mark for adding answer to $\frac{3}{8}$; 1 mark for correct answer. Total 3 marks.*

*See page 11, Calculating with fractions 1 and page 12, Calculating with fractions 2*

**22.** 1st graph: $y = x^2$; 2nd graph: $y = \frac{1}{x}$

3rd graph: $y = x$; 4th graph: $y = x^3$

*1 mark for any two equations matched to the correct graphs; 1 mark if all correct.*

*See page 44, Cubic and reciprocal graphs*

**23.** Mass = density × volume = $700 \times 0.5$

$= 350\,\text{kg} = 350\,000\,\text{g}$

*1 mark for 700 × 0.5; 1 mark for 350; 1 mark for correct answer of 350 000. Total 3 marks.*

*See page 56, Compound measures*

**24. a** −3 is the first missing number since it must occur more than once.

The mean is 7, so the total of all the numbers is

$7 \times 7 = 49$

Other missing number is

$49 - (-3 - 3 + 1 + 4 + 7 + 32) = 11$

*1 mark for each missing number.*

**b** Range = 32 − (−3) = 35

*1 mark for correct answer circled.*

**c** Median = 4

Mode is unsuitable as it gives the lowest value in the list.

Mean is unsuitable as 32 is an outlier.

Median is the best choice as it doesn't use outliers.

*1 mark for calculating median; 1 mark for mentioning outliers; 1 mark for correct answer and reason.*

*Total 3 marks.*

*See page 97, Averages and spread*

**25.** $\frac{1}{2}$

*1 mark for correct answer circled.*

*See page 90, Exact values*

**26.** $x = 180° − 45° − 60° = 75°$

$y = 180° − 60° − 75° = 45°$

(Angles in a triangle sum to 180°.)

The two triangles have equal angles.

However, Blair is correct as the lengths of the sides of the triangles are not known. For the triangles to be congruent, the corresponding sides should be the same length.

*1 mark for calculating missing angles; 1 mark for identifying that both triangles have identical angles; 1 mark for correct answer with justification. Full marks awarded for correct solution with no angles calculated.*

*Total 3 marks.*

*See page 71, Congruent shapes*

**27.** Percentage increase in price for large vs. small

$= \frac{(90 − 75)}{75} × 100\% = \frac{15}{75} × 100\% = 20\%$

The number of sweets increases by 25% and the cost increases by 20%, so the large bag is better value.

*1 mark for an attempt to find the % increase in the price e.g. $\frac{(90 − 75)}{75} × 100$; 1 mark for 20%; 1 mark for comparison with correct conclusion i.e. large bag is better value.*

*Total 3 marks.*

*See page 50, Proportion*

**28.** $(2 × 10^4) × (2 × 10^2)^2 = (2 × 10^4) × (4 × 10^4) = (8 × 10^8)$

*1 mark for a correct first step i.e. $(2 × 10^2)^2 = 4 × 10^4$; 1 mark for correct final answer in standard form.*

*See page 20, Calculating with standard form*

**29.** Difference in number of 'parts' = 7 − 2 = 5

5 parts = 60 cm; 1 part = 60 ÷ 5 = 12 cm

Length of wood = total number of parts × 12

$= (2 + 7) × 12 = 9 × 12 = 108$ cm

*1 mark for 5 parts = 60 cm; 1 mark for 9 × (60 ÷ 5) or equivalent; 1 mark for correct answer. Total 3 marks.*

*See page 52, Using ratio*

## Paper 2 Calculator

**1.** 25 × 10 = 250 mm

*1 mark for correct answer circled.*

*See page 60, Measures*

**2.** 29

*1 mark for correct answer circled.*

*See page 17, Prime factor decomposition*

**3.** 0.45

*1 mark for correct answer circled.*

*See page 13, Fractions, decimals, percentages*

**4.** $x = 12 + 5$

$x = 17$

*1 mark for correct answer circled.*

*See page 26, Solving linear equations*

**5.** 0.07  0.077  0.7  0.707

*1 mark for all in correct order.*

*See page 1, Place value*

**6. a** False. 27 is a cube number.

**b** False. 2 and 6 are both factors of 12

**c** True. 6 and 15 are the only triangular numbers in the list.

*1 mark for each correct answer with correct reason.*

*See page 16, Factors and multiples*

**7.** Total cost = £7.20 × 2 + £32.50 = £46.90

Amount left = £50 − £46.90 = £3.10

Astrid is correct.

*1 mark for £46.90; 1 mark for subtracting total from 50; 1 mark for correct conclusion with working. Total 3 marks.*

*See page 8, Calculating with decimals*

**8.** Length on map = 34.5 ÷ 5 = 6.9 cm

*1 mark for attempt to work out proportion; 1 mark for correct answer.*

*See page 61, Scale drawing*

**9.** Ingrid needs to multiply out the brackets first, so

$3 + 2(x + 4) = 3 + 2x + 8 = 11 + 2x$

*1 mark for a clear and correct explanation.*

*See page 29, Expanding single brackets*

**10.** Pressure = force ÷ area = 900 ÷ 200 = 4.5 N/cm²

*1 mark for attempt to use correct formula; 1 mark for correct answer.*

*See page 56, Compound measures*

**11. a**

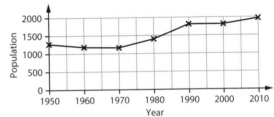

*1 mark for at least 4 correctly plotted points; 1 mark for all correct and points joined with straight lines.*

**b** The general trend is increasing.

*1 mark for correct answer.*

*See page 102, Time series*

**12.** $\frac{1.25}{4.57} (= 0.2735...) = 0.27$ to 2 dp

*1 mark for $\frac{1.25}{4.57}$ or 0.2735... or equivalent; 1 mark for correct answer of 0.27.*

*See page 7, Calculating with negative numbers*

**13. a** $−t$

*1 mark for correct answer.*

**b** $y^3$

*1 mark for correct answer.*

**c** $3x^2$

*1 mark for correct answer.*

**d** $2z$

*1 mark for $2z^k$ for any $k ≠ 0$; 1 mark for fully correct.*

*See page 22, Simplifying expressions*

**14.** $40:60 = 1:\frac{60}{40} = 1:1.5$

*1 mark for correct answer circled.*

*See page 51, Ratio*

**15.** Let $x$ be the side length.
Volume $= x^3 = 450$
$x = \sqrt[3]{450} = 7.66309\ldots$
Area $= 6x^2 = 6(7.66309\ldots)^2$
$\qquad = 352\,\text{cm}^2$ (to the nearest whole number)
***1 mark*** *for correct formula for side length or volume;*
***1 mark*** *for squaring side length and multiplying by 6;*
***1 mark*** *for correct rounded answer;* ***1 mark*** *for correct units. Total 4 marks.*
***See page 78, 3D shapes***

**16. a**

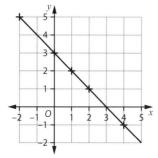

  ***1 mark*** *for at least 3 points plotted correctly;* ***1 mark*** *for fully correct and straight line drawn.*

  **b** Gradient $= \frac{\text{change in } y}{\text{change in } x} = -1$
  Line crosses $y$-axis at 3
  Equation of line is $y = -x + 3$
  ***1 mark*** *for attempt to use* $\frac{\text{change in } y}{\text{change in } x}$; ***1 mark*** *for correct gradient;* ***1 mark*** *for correct equation (or equivalent equation e.g.* $y = 3 - x, x + y = 3$*). Total 3 marks.*

  **c** When $x = 97$, $y = -97 + 3 = -94$
  So, $(97, -100)$ will not lie on the line.
  ***1 mark*** *for substituting* $x = 97$ *or* $y = -100$ *into your equation;* ***1 mark*** *for correct conclusion with correct working.*
  ***See page 40, Equation of a straight line***

**17.** Total frequencies $= 60$
Boat frequency $= 60 - (15 + 25 + 5 + 7) = 8$
Each angle $=$ frequency $\times 6$ (since angles sum to $360°$)
Angles are $90°, 150°, 30°, 42°, 48°$

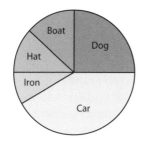

***1 mark*** *for missing frequency;* ***1 mark*** *for any correct angle calculated;* ***1 mark*** *for any correct angle drawn;* ***1 mark*** *for at least 3 correct angles correctly drawn;* ***1 mark*** *for fully correct including labels. Total 5 marks.*
***See page 96, Pie charts***

**18.** $15 \div 12 = 1.25$
So, Delia needs $1.25 \times 100\,\text{g} = 125\,\text{g}$ flour ($< 130\,\text{g}$, ok),
$1.25 \times 2 = 2.5$ large eggs ($< 3$, ok),
$1.25 \times 300\,\text{ml} = 375\,\text{ml}$ milk ($> 350\,\text{ml}$).
She does not have enough for 15 pancakes: she does not have enough milk.
***1 mark*** *for* $15 \div 12 \,(= 1.25)$; ***1 mark*** *for multiplying by 1.25;* ***1 mark*** *for correct conclusion supported by fully correct calculation. Total 3 marks.*
***See page 51, Ratio***

**19. a** $4x + 12x^2 = 4x(1 + 3x)$
  ***1 mark*** *for 4 or x outside brackets;* ***1 mark*** *for fully correct answer.*
  **b** $x^2 + 5x - 6 = x^2 + 6x - x - 6 = (x + 6)(x - 1)$
  ***1 mark*** *for brackets with* $x$ *and two numbers that multiply to give* $-6$; ***1 mark*** *for the correct answer.*
  ***See page 30, Factorising into single brackets and page 32, Factorising into double brackets***

**20.** Original price $\times 0.8 = £44.80$
So, original price $= \frac{44.80}{0.8} = £56$
This is not £53.76, so the sign is incorrect.
***1 mark*** *for using 0.8 as a multiplier or for stating that £44.80 = 80%;* ***1 mark*** *for* $\frac{44.80}{0.8}$ *or equivalent;* ***1 mark*** *for correct conclusion with correct reason. Total 3 marks. Note that there are alternative methods.*
***See page 55, Original value problems***

**21.** Only the value of the indices should change.
So, $ab = 2^4 \times 3^7$
***1 mark*** *for a clear explanation e.g. 'the base doesn't change' etc. or for saying that the answer should be* $2^4 \times 3^7$
***See page 15, Calculating with indices***

**22.** Bearing of $A$ from $B$ is $80° + 180° = 260°$
***1 mark*** *for correct answer circled.*
***See page 64, Bearings***

**23.** Class 3A has a greater median, so their scores are higher on average.
Class 3B has a lower range, so their scores are more consistent.
***1 mark*** *for comparing medians in context e.g. 'Average scores lower for 3B';* ***1 mark*** *for comparing ranges in context e.g. '3A are less consistent'.*
***See page 97, Averages and spread***

**24.** 4 hours and 20 minutes $= 4\frac{1}{3}$ hours
Speed $= 440 \div 4\frac{1}{3} = 101.538\ldots = 101.5\,\text{km/h}$ to 1 dp
***1 mark*** *for converting 20 minutes to* $\frac{1}{3}$ *hours;* ***1 mark*** *for dividing distance by time;* ***1 mark*** *for correct answer to 1 dp. Total 3 marks.*
***See page 56, Compound measures***

**25.** $12\,742\,000\,\text{m} = 1.2742 \times 10^7$
$1.42984 \times 10^8 = 14.2984 \times 10^7$
Comparing the numbers written as multiples of the same power of 10 shows the diameter of Jupiter is closer to 10 times ($14.2984 \div 1.2742$) the diameter of Earth, not 1000 times. Sebastian is wrong.
***1 mark*** *for converting first number to standard form;* ***1 mark*** *for comparing both numbers;* ***1 mark*** *for correct conclusion and reason. Total 3 marks.*
*Note that there are alternative methods.*
***See page 20, Calculating with standard form***

**26. a** First attempt miss: $1 - 0.3 = 0.7$ (left)
  First attempt hit, second attempt miss: $1 - 0.4 = 0.6$ (top right)
  First attempt miss, second attempt hit: $1 - 0.7 = 0.3$ (bottom right)
  ***1 mark*** *for any correct probability;* ***1 mark*** *for all correct.*
  **b** P(two hits) $= 0.3 \times 0.4 = 0.12$
  ***1 mark*** *for multiplying;* ***1 mark*** *for correct answer.*
  ***See page 108, Tree diagrams***

**27.** $25\% = \frac{1}{4}$ (= white)

$\frac{1}{4} + \frac{1}{6} = \frac{3}{12} + \frac{2}{12} = \frac{5}{12}$

$1 - \frac{5}{12} = \frac{7}{12}$ (= green)

Red : green $= \frac{2}{12} : \frac{7}{12} = 2 : 7$

***1 mark** for converting percentage and fraction to same form; **1 mark** for adding and then subtracting from 1; **1 mark** for correct answer in correct order. Total 3 marks.*

***See page 52, Using ratio***

**28. a** $0.865 \leq x < 0.875$

***1 mark** for 0.865 or 0.875 at correct end of an error interval; **1 mark** for fully correct.*

**b** $7 \leq y < 8$

***1 mark** for 7 or 8 at correct end of an error interval; **1 mark** for fully correct.*

***See page 6, Error intervals***

**29.** Volume $= \pi r^2 h$

$1000 = \pi r^3$

$r = \sqrt[3]{\frac{1000}{\pi}} = 6.827\ldots = 6.8\,\text{cm to 1 dp}$

***1 mark** for attempt to use $\pi r^3$; **1 mark** for $\sqrt[3]{\frac{1000}{\pi}}$ (= 6.827…); **1 mark** for 6.8. Total 3 marks.*

***See page 81, Prisms and cylinders***

**30.**

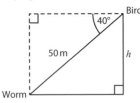

$h = 50 \sin 40° = 32.139\ldots = 32°$ to 2 sf

***1 mark** for use of sin 40° (or cos 50°); **1 mark** for 50 sin 40° (= 32.139…); **1 mark** for correct answer to 2 sf. Total 3 marks.*

***See page 88, Trigonometry 1***

## Paper 3 Calculator

**1.** $4^5 = 1024$

***1 mark** for correct answer circled.*

***See page 14, Powers and roots***

**2.** $\frac{3}{100}$

***1 mark** for correct answer circled.*

***See page 13, Fractions, decimals, percentages***

**3.** 1.5 litres

***1 mark** for correct answer circled.*

***See page 60, Measures***

**4.** $-2t$

***1 mark** for correct answer circled.*

***See page 22, Simplifying expressions***

**5.** $64 (= 8^2 = 4^3)$

***1 mark** for correct answer circled.*

***See page 14, Powers and roots***

**6.** 2 out of 5 (= 3 + 2) pieces are white.

Total number of pieces is $25 = 5 \times 5$

The number of white pieces is $2 \times 5 = 10$

***1 mark** for 2 out of 5; **1 mark** for correct answer of 10*

***See page 52, Using ratio***

**7.** $28 - 3 - 4 = 21$

$\frac{21}{28} \times 100\% = 75\%$

Jonas is correct.

***1 mark** for 21; **1 mark** for $\frac{21}{28} \times 100\%$ (= 75%); **1 mark** for correct conclusion with correct working. Total 3 marks.*

***See page 103, Theoretical probability***

**8.** 10:30 + 20 minutes = 10:50

$10:50 + 1\frac{1}{4}$ = 11:50 + 15 minutes = 12:05

***1 mark** for correct answer circled.*

***See page 59, Time and timetables***

**9.** Protractors:

$4 \times$ (buy 5 get 6th free) = 24 protractors for the price of 20

So, for 25 protractors, Vicky must pay for 21

$21 \times 12p = £2.52$

Sticky tape:

$2 \times$ (10 rolls for £2) = 20 rolls for £4

So, for 25 rolls, Vicky must pay £4 + 5 × 24p = £5.20

Pencil sharpeners:

$12 \times$ (buy 1 get 2nd half-price) = 24 pencil sharpeners.

So, Vicky must pay 13 × 18p + 12 × 9p = £3.42

Total cost = £2.52 + £5.20 + £3.42 = £11.14

***1 mark** for a correct strategy to buy 25 protractors (= £2.52) or 25 sticky tape (= £5.20) or 25 pencil sharpeners (= £3.42);*

***1 mark** for two correct strategies; **1 mark** for adding your three amounts; **1 mark** for correct final answer. Total 4 marks.*

***See page 50, Proportion***

**10. a** 11 to 30 is 20 integers

P(choose 25) $= \frac{1}{20}$

***1 mark** for correct answer or equivalent e.g. 0.05*

**b** P(choose 1) = 0

***1 mark** for correct answer.*

**c** The multiples of 3 are 12, 15, 18, 21, 24, 27, 30

P(choose multiple of 3) $= \frac{7}{20}$

***1 mark** for correct answer or equivalent e.g. 0.35*

**d** P(two-digit number) = 1

***1 mark** for correct answer.*

***See page 103, Theoretical probability***

**11. a** It is a Fibonacci sequence, so each term is the sum of the previous two.

Next terms:

$4 + 7 = 11$

$7 + 11 = 18$

***1 mark** for correct answer.*

**b** It is a geometric sequence, so you multiply (or divide) by a constant number to go from term-to-term. The rule is divide by 2

***1 mark** for correct answer or equivalent e.g. multiply by 0.5*

**c** 7, __, 3

It is an arithmetic sequence, so the difference between terms in constant.

The difference between the 1st and 3rd term is −4, so the difference between each term is −2

4th term is $3 - 2 = 1$

***1 mark** for constant difference −2; **1 mark** for correct answer.*

***Page 46, Sequences and page 49, Special sequences***

**12.** There are double the people, so it will take half the time.

$19 \div 2 = 9.5$ days

***1 mark** for dividing by 2; **1 mark** for correct answer.*

***See page 58, Inverse proportion***

**13.** $x = (1 - 9) \div 4 = -2$

*1 mark for correct answer circled.*

**See page 25, Functions**

**14.** Angle $ABC = 110°$ because corresponding angles are equal and $AB$ and $DC$ are parallel.

Base angles of isoceles $ABC$ are equal and angle sum of triangle is $180°$.

So, angle $BCA = (180° - 110°) \div 2 = 35°$

*1 mark for 110 and corresponding angles; 1 mark for attempting to subtract from 180 and divide by 2; 1 mark for correct answer. Total 3 marks.*

**See page 63, Angle rules**

**15. a** $\frac{\sqrt{66}}{3.4^3} = 0.206\,697\,4966$

*1 mark for 66 seen or implied; 1 mark for correct answer. (It's a good idea to estimate these to check your answer is sensible: $\frac{\sqrt{64}}{3^3} \approx \frac{8}{27} \approx 0.3$.)*

**b** 0.207

*1 mark for correct answer.*

**See page 2, Order of operations and page 4, Significant figures**

**16.**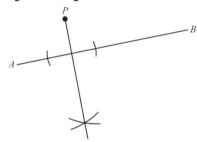

*1 mark for arcs intersecting line segment $AB$; 1 mark for intersecting arcs below line segment $AB$; 1 mark for fully complete with perpendicular drawn from $P$ to $AB$. Total 3 marks.*

**See page 85, Perpendiculars and bisectors**

**17. a** $A \cap B = \{e, a, r, s\}$

**b** $A \cup B = \{p, e, a, r, s, o, n, g\}$

*1 mark for each correct answer.*

**See page 109, Set notation**

**18.** Curved perimeter $= \frac{2\pi r}{2} = 6\pi$

Perimeter of semicircle $= 6\pi + 12$

$= 30.8495...$

$= 30.85$ cm to 2 dp

*1 mark for $\frac{2\pi r}{2} = 6\pi$; 1 mark for adding 12 to your curved perimeter; 1 mark for correct answer to 2 dp. Total 3 marks.*

**See page 76, Semicircles**

**19.** Let perpendicular height be $h$.

Base of right-angled triangle $= \frac{4.8}{2} = 2.4$

$h^2 + 2.4^2 = 5.3^2$

$h^2 = 5.3^2 - 2.4^2$

$h = 4.73$ cm to 3 sf

*1 mark for $5.3^2 - 2.4^2 (= 22.33)$; 1 mark for taking the square root (= 4.725...); 1 mark for correct answer to 3 sf. Total 3 marks.*

**See page 87, Pythagoras' theorem**

**20.** £1 = \$1.31; £24 = 1.31 × 24 = \$31.44 > \$30

The T-shirt is cheaper in the US. He should buy it in the US.

*1 mark for converting £24 into \$ or \$30 into £; 1 mark for comparison of values with correct conclusion.*

**See page 57, Direct proportion**

**21.** The fraction of people who brought a phone is $\frac{3}{4} = 0.75$

Multiplier for phones left on $= 1 - 0.9 = 0.1$

Let $p$ be the number of people in the audience.

$0.75 \times 0.1 \times p = 84$

$p = 84 \div 0.1 \div 0.75 = 1120$

*1 mark for 0.75 or 0.1 or equivalent; 1 mark for equation using your factors; 1 mark for correct answer. Total 3 marks.*

**See page 55, Original value problems**

**22. a** $36 = 4 \times 9 = 2^2 \times 3^2$

$80 = 8 \times 10 = 2^4 \times 5$

LCM $= 2^4 \times 3^2 \times 5 = 720$

*1 mark for either prime factor decomposition; 1 mark for correct answer.*

**b** $80 = 2^4 \times 5$

$24 = 2^3 \times 3$

HCF $= 2^3 = 8$

*1 mark for correct answer circled.*

**See page 18, Finding HCF and LCM**

**23. a** There are 67 data values in total, so the median is the 34th value.

The 34th value lies in the $30 < t \le 40$ interval.

*1 mark for $30 < t \le 40$*

**b** Sheena has chosen 7 because it appears twice in the table. However, the mode is the time that has the highest frequency, so the mode (or modal class) is the $30 < t \le 40$ interval.

*1 mark for clear explanation of Sheena's error.*

**c i**

| Frequency | Midpoint | Frequency × midpoint |
|---|---|---|
| 13 | 5 | 65 |
| 7 | 15 | 105 |
| 12 | 25 | 300 |
| 28 | 35 | 980 |
| 7 | 45 | 315 |
| Total = 67 | | Total = 1765 |

Estimated mean $= 1765 \div 67 = 26.343...$

$= 26.3$ to 1 dp

*1 mark for at least one correct midpoint; 1 mark for multiplying frequency by midpoint; 1 mark for dividing total of frequency × midpoint by total frequency; 1 mark for correct answer to 1 dp. Total 4 marks.*

**ii** It is an estimate because the times are not given explicitly. They are only given as class intervals.

*1 mark for any clear explanation as to why the mean can only be an estimate e.g. 'only using midpoints'.*

**See page 99, Grouped data**

**24. a** $2x + 2y$

*1 mark for correct answer circled.*

**b** $x = 2y$ and area $A = xy$, so $A = 2y^2$

$2y^2 = 20; y^2 = 10; y = \sqrt{10}$

$x = 2 \times \sqrt{10} = 6.32$ cm to 3 sf

*1 mark for $x = 2y$ or $A = xy$; 1 mark for $2y^2 = 20$ and attempt to solve; 1 mark for correct $y$; 1 mark for correct answer (accept unrounded or different rounding for answer of 6.324 555...). Total 4 marks.*

**See page 73, Area and perimeter**

**25.**

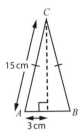

Base of right-angled triangle $= \frac{6}{2} = 3$

$\cos CAB = \frac{3}{15}$

$CAB = \cos^{-1}\left(\frac{3}{15}\right) = 78.5°$ to 1 dp

*__1 mark__ for $\cos CAB = \frac{3}{15}$; __1 mark__ for taking the inverse (= 78.46…); __1 mark__ for correct answer to 1 dp. Total 3 marks.*

***See page 89, Trigonometry 2***

**26. a** $2x - 5 \le 7 - x$; $3x - 5 \le 7$; $3x \le 12$; $x \le 4$

*__1 mark__ for a correct algebraic step; __1 mark__ for final answer of $x \le 4$. (Note the inequality symbol must be used in final answer.)*

**b**

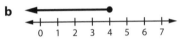

*__1 mark__ for number line with solid circle at 4 with line in the direction shown.*

**c** $-3 < 3n \le 9$

$-1 < n \le 3$

Integer values for $n$ are 0, 1, 2 and 3

*__1 mark__ for $-1 < n \le 3$ or equivalent, e.g. $n > -1$ and $n \le 3$; __1 mark__ for correct final answer.*

***See page 37, Solving inequalities***

**27.** Multiplier for 3% increase is 1.03

Let the original amount be $x$.

$x \times 1.03 = £711.22$

$x = £711.22 \div 1.03 = £690.50$

The original amount was £690.50

*__1 mark__ for $x \times 1.03 = £711.22$ or equivalent; __1 mark__ for correct final answer.*

***See page 55, Original value problems***

**28. a** It doesn't eliminate either variable.

*__1 mark__ for explanation that neither variable is eliminated.*

**b** $2x - 3y = 16$ (1); $5x - 3y = 31$ (2)

Subtracting (1) from (2): $3x = 15$; $x = 5$

Substituting into (1): $10 - 3y = 16$;

$3y = -6$; $y = -2$

The solutions are $x = 5$ and $y = -2$

*__1 mark__ for subtracting the equations to eliminate the $y$ terms; __1 mark__ for solving for $x$; __1 mark__ for fully correct solution. Total 3 marks.*

***See page 35, Simultaneous equations 1***

**29.** Enlargement, scale factor 2, from centre of enlargement $(-4, 4)$

*__1 mark__ for enlargement; __1 mark__ for scale factor 2; __1 mark__ for $(-4, 4)$. Total 3 marks.*

***See page 70, Enlargement***

# My notes

# My notes

# My notes

# My notes

## OXFORD
### UNIVERSITY PRESS

Great Clarendon Street, Oxford, OX2 6DP, United Kingdom

Oxford University Press is a department of the University of Oxford.

It furthers the University's objective of excellence in research, scholarship, and education by publishing worldwide. Oxford is a registered trade mark of Oxford University Press in the UK and in certain other countries

British Library Cataloguing in Publication Data
Data available

978-1-38-200646-0

10 9 8 7 6 5 4 3 2 1

Paper used in the production of this book is a natural, recyclable product made from wood grown in sustainable forests.

The manufacturing process conforms to the environmental regulations of the country of origin.

Printed in the United Kingdom by Bell and Bain Ltd, Glasgow

### Acknowledgements
Authors: Paul Hunt and Jemma Sherwood
Series Editor: Naomi Bartholomew-Millar
Editorial team: Dom Holdsworth and Rosie Day
With thanks to Katie Wood, Ross Everson and Rachel Phillipson for their contributions.

The publisher would like to thank the following for permissions to use copyright material:

Cover illustrations: Cristina Romero Palma / Shutterstock, Rachael Arnott / Shutterstock

Artwork: QBS Media Services Inc.

Although we have made every effort to trace and contact all copyright holders before publication this has not been possible in all cases. If notified, the publisher will rectify any errors or omissions at the earliest opportunity.

Links to third party websites are provided by Oxford in good faith and for information only. Oxford disclaims any responsibility for the materials contained in any third party website referenced in this work.